Liberation

Liberation - Breaking The Glass Ceiling Of Society
Edited & Compiled by Samhitha Reddy
Print Edition

First Published in India in 2021
Inkfeathers Publishing
New Delhi 110095

ISBN 978-81-950205-9-1

www.inkfeathers.com

Liberation

Breaking the Glass Ceiling of Society

Edited & Compiled by

SAMHITHA REDDY

Inkfeathers Publishing

DISCLAIMER

The anthology "Liberation- Breaking The Glass Ceiling Of Society" is a collection of 46 poems and 26 stories by 44 authors who belong to different parts of the globe. The anthology editor and the publisher have edited the content provided by the co-authors to enhance the experience for readers and make it free of plagiarism as much as possible. Unless otherwise indicated, all the names, characters, objects, businesses, places, events, incidents — whether physical/non-physical, real/unreal, tangible/ intangible in whatsoever description used in this book are either the product of the author's imagination or used in a fictitious manner. Any resemblance to actual persons, objects, entities, living or dead, or actual events is purely coincidental. The poems and stories published in this book are solely owned by their respective authors and are no way intended to hurt anyone's religious, political, spiritual, brand, personal or fanatic beliefs and/or faith, whatsoever.

In case, any sort of plagiarism is detected in the poems and stories within this anthology or in case of any complaints or grievances or objections, neither the anthology editor, nor the publisher are to be held responsible for any such claims. The author(s) who holds the rights to the poem(s) and/or story(s), shall be held responsible, whatsoever.

CO-AUTHORED BY

Sushree Diya Om | Samyuktha Ramachandran | Baishakhi Mukherjee | Sarvesh Shyam | Arthi P | Suhas Ramegowda | Chantal Espitalier – Noel | Deepa Ragunathan | Sitara Kumbale | Sumati Mohan | Nirosha Tomy | Dr. R. Uma Sharma | Lakshmi Priyanga M. | Rakshita Nagaraj | Amala L. | Maria Mappilassery | Neha Prashar Verma | Padma | Aryaman Chakraborty | Minnu Ranjith | Namrada Varshini | Nalini Vipin | Christina Triplett-Wagenknecht | Divya Om Manoharan | Riya Om | Sujitha Ryali | Nitya Bhatia | Ambika Rao | Maria Wynnyckyj | Soham Maliye | Maxine Mathew | Komal R. D. | Munmun Aidasani | Renee Mary Jetto | Christine J. | Divya Naveen | Joshuanna Woods | Soumya Gudiyella | Tejasvi Rajesh | Vidya Shivaram | Sabhyata Bhandari | Anju Anil | Asleena Argyris | Prerna Agrawal

CONTENTS

ELYSIAN FIELDS

IN RAPTURES

UP IN ARMS

HEAVY HEART

IN ECLIPSE

ABOUT THE EDITOR

Samhitha Reddy

Samhitha Reddy is a law graduate who is currently pursuing her MSc. in Human Rights at the London School of Economics and Political Science, London. As an aspiring lawyer, she wishes to pursue a career in international human rights and has been widely published in various leading law journals of India. A wanderer at heart, she is also an avid traveller and foodie. She has a growing passion for Indian mythology and history and is trying her hand at writing fiction. As a part of her first editorial venture, she has curated a two-volume anthology titled, "Shades of a Woman: Navigating Society as a Woman", and "Liberation: Breaking the Glass Ceiling of Society", where the writers share their experiences and inspiring stories about the women in their lives (or themselves) and their navigation through social structures and barriers. She is now curating another anthology titled "Deviant: Chronicles of Pride" that is aimed at raising awareness about and acceptance of the LGBTQIA+ community. A bookworm ever since she was young, it is hard to find her without a book in her hands and she's now chasing her dream of being a published author in addition to pursuing her passion for human rights.

EDITOR'S NOTE

I've been a fan of literature for as long as I can remember, but this is a theme that is extremely close to my heart. Perhaps it is because of my experiences as a woman or the cumulative experiences of the women around me; our stories often go untold, or we find ourselves without the right platform to express them.

The contributors to this anthology come from various walks of life, many of whom have drawn inspiration from their personal experiences in different parts of this country and across the world. Students, homemakers, entrepreneurs, leaders, and even professional authors have poured their hearts out into these pieces and contributed to this wonderfully diverse and poignant treasury of poetry and prose. From real personal experiences to incredible creations of their imagination, this anthology showcases heartfelt and awe-inspiring stories of women who have strived to be better, not just for their friends and families, but also for themselves.

Join me on this enchanting and tumultuous journey with a rollercoaster of emotions of determination, perseverance, anger, joy, sadness, and love. An incredible compilation of stories and poetry of mothers, daughters, sisters, grandmothers, and wives, that truly encapsulates what it means to be a woman in today's society.

I would like to thank Inkfeathers for giving me this wonderful opportunity and the amazing people who have contributed to this anthology, many of whom I am now proud to call my friends. I hope that through these stories that cover a myriad of emotions, the readers can relate and have a look into the various aspects of a woman's life and appreciate the expansive array of the shades of a woman.

ELYSIAN
FIELDS

1

Who I Am Today

The hand that broke my slate of grey
The face that breathed the wrath of day
The one who with that stern face swayed
He made me who I am today

Might I have held the fire of ire
Might I have crumbled at the fear
But what if
I chose instead
To walk on, clear
To tread the path of love, not dread

Might I be as strong as this
To shed all that had held me back
To rise above the pain of him
For,
No matter what I'd hoped from him
He made me who I am today

And who am I?
I am That
Strong and Kind
Woman and Wise
And one who walks the path of Light
And so, I thank him for the pain

It made me who I am today

by Sushree Diya Om

2

Mother Earth

She had warmth in her eyes, and depth in her gaze
When she entered a room, she swept all in it with an easy grace
That's the prelude for the unconditional love of the mother
Whose interminable authenticity plans to stay

Soft, gentle, and vast, the protector of all
Lived a life of servitude propped up within gold clad walls
Altruist and nourishing, with energy for all lucky enough to see
Only asked for small acts of kindness in return, Hindu mythology calls her 'Devi'

Skilled in many decrees, with the creativity to build, give life, and cherish
Brought dance, healing, and energy, forever the hopeful enthusiast
Belief in the majority, no judgment to befall
Moments of childlike wide-eyed innocence with a spring in her step like a doll

The breaking of boundaries, and destroyer of chains
In this long, wise, existence, she's known many a pain
Of treacherous fires, from foe, family, and friend,

Cut at her roots, her very existence, she thought the humiliation would never end

The golden touch of her finger filled many with energy
Gazing at the entropy, she prayed and forgave earnestly
Earth learned the power of spirit, and the freedom of breaking free
Acceptance, kindness, and benevolence of another degree

'An eye for an eye' comes the phrase, but she chose to not pay heed
Walked out there and simply proved them wrong with her various deeds
'Behave like a woman', demure and sweet
Yes, behave like this woman; she's both warrior and saint, in a melee

Fire in her eyes, water in her soul, wind in her grace, and the earth below her feet
All of the elements come together to show thee
That woman can be you, and that woman can be me
The saviour of all, and strength personified, is my mother to me.

by Samyuktha Ramachandran

3

I Believe

They say I don't cry enough,
They say I don't grieve.
They don't know that's how I keep you alive,
That's how I keep my belief!

by Baishakhi Mukherjee

4

I Am Falling In Love… Again

Is it okay to fall in love…again?
Is it too soon… to be in love?
Should I wait some more…to confirm?
Should I ask my heart…to be sure?
Should I think…before I laugh?
Should I check…before I hum?
Should I tell others…or should I hide?
Will people judge…if they know?
That am falling in love… with life… again!

by Baishakhi Mukherjee

5

A Tale Of Fire

They Breathed life into our lungs and passed on their
wisdom, all the while being shackled to society's whims
Taught their daughters to be independent, strong, and free;
Internally whispered 'you will not live like me',
Externally positing 'darling, life is too short to not live your
dream'.

'Be like transcendental fire, fierce and bright'
'Fire doesn't know how to give up without a fight'
Not when betrayal came in its mightiest form
Her daughter looked within and accepted a difficult and
challenging norm.

Fire tamed herself as only a strong woman can
Moulded, changed, even adopted another religion
And when her choices were taken away by silent force
'Love can conquer all', she lived by her gentle oath.

'It makes me strong, not weak', she chanted fiercely
Broken, battered, and bruised, externally, and internally
Realization that rejection of the soul, body and mind was the
worst kind of agony
Innocence and broken dreams were the punishment of
forsaken naiveté.

A remnant of her mother's voice gently said 'the world
cannot take your flame, look within'
'Fight for your freedom, your peace, your spirit, only you
can'
'Pick yourself up from the pain and punishment of this real
world'
'You are everlasting and infinite, my precious little girl'

Grieve as she would and grieve as she did while she fought
the demons of battered dreams, livid and filled with chagrin
'Why me, why now', how will I survive' 'Is this my fate, is
my flame doomed to die?'

Faint stirrings of a voice (this time her own) said 'believe in
yourself'
'Find the strength to move on, you cannot allow your own
diminishment'
She took her happiness into her own hands, one step
forward and then half a dozen
Strong, brilliant, dazzling, kind, beautiful, ambitious, and
confident

'I choose me' she said, and opened a company
They didn't think she would, said it wasn't a part of her
destiny
'I choose me' she said, her flame glittering strong, brilliant,
incandescently
Empowered herself to the strongest version of herself she
could be

My beautiful ladies, what is important to remember is that nothing and no one can tame a natural fire

by Samyuktha Ramachandran

6

A Tale Of Wind And Water

She's water: calm and soothing, no matter how treacherous
the world can be
Flowing in and flow out, resistance cannot bring ease
Concerns of family, health, pressure, and expectations in
existence, sure as can be
Calmly she flows, adjustments and acceptance are a
necessity.

Authenticity of heart: patient, and kind
The ability to love, with no judgment in her mind
A voice of reason to all, and a pillar of strength
Expanses of wisdom and insight, of various lengths.

Graceful and flowing waves, it was a choice to keep her
peace
Under the surface lay the ability to be a fearsome beast
Who she chose to indulge with positive creativity
Water is authentic, accepting, and brave, it's imbibed in her
personality.

A vision of grace, she didn't need a form
With beautiful shades of blue, white, and green, not to be
tempered by any storm
Expansive, and deep, her energy flows endlessly

Artist and painter, with the ability to relate and create, she can build anything architecturally.

Wind lay under water, blowing and trying to find her way through her tears
Continuous patterns of betrayal from those she holds dear
Not always with a support system to hold near
Climbed her way to the top of mountain and looked down with fear.

Fear of failing rippled around her,' if I jump, will I fall or fly?'
She chose to not feel alone, determined 'I won't know unless I try'
The beauty of the wind is that her strength will always remain a mystery
Sound of mind, and warm of heart, with a deep sense of loyalty.

And with that she surrendered to the natural breeze
The problems are too far away, her evolved being is now always at ease
The worst that could happen happened and she's still alive
Stronger than any barrier is her will to survive.

Water and wind touch each other, like two old souls anew
Lucky enough to touch them, learn from them and be loved by them, there are a very few.

by Samyuktha Ramachandran

7

Of Thunder And Lightning

To my friends
The great women in my life
Who have to look over their shoulder
Constantly and ever so often
Alert to the jackals lurking
And of people judging
At a flawed society and its expectation
Some, their own family, with hesitation
To my friends
The great women in my life
For whatever it's worth
I want you to know
You are not alone
You are not less
You are not what society makes you out to be
In a system that's a glorified mess
You are so much more
You are an ocean
Of love
Of light
Of wonder
And might
To the roar of thunder
And the strike of lightning
Shall you right their blunder

Rip off the noose they're tightening
This world is yours to plunder
May your glory be frightening!

by Sarvesh Shyam

8

Some Day

Someday I will take some rest.
Someday when the burden is less.
Someday I will shed my tears.
Someday when the pain will grow less.
Someday I will have my cry, some day.

by Baishakhi Mukherjee

9

I Saw You

I saw you in a dream,
And I saw that you have moved on....
And it made me happy,
It made me feel at peace.
You looked so calm,
You looked so serene,
You took a deep breath and raised your hands,
I kept looking at you waiting for you to turn.
And then you looked around and you smiled at the world,
And you looked at me, but you didn't see me,
You had a beard that you never had before,
You looked so handsome and you looked so happy,
And I kept standing there watching you smile....

by Baishakhi Mukherjee

10

#Undo Everything

#Uncelebrate the day with gifts and flowers on a single day!!
For what use are these, you are a diva every single day :)
#Unstoppable a soaring eagle, you should be!
You own your destiny, dare anyone stop thee?
#Undaunted you should be by this judgmental society
Useless tongues waddle, nothing but fake empathy
#Undress your habit of infinite tolerance
Why are you feeding their constant ignorance?
#Unconventional is your simplest of the ideas
You can even brave a storm, be that Bad Ass!!
#Unapologetic to your actions, defines Independence
You and just you can overcome this defiance
#Unplug from being called a stereotype
Fight and rise as a phoenix, an archetype
#Unlearn blaming others for your plight
Bring out your best, there is no need of fright
#Unsuitable you look to this world
They are yet to educate themselves to come out of the fold
#Unorthodox are your ways of treading life's ocean
Live it the fullest, it's the best time before we drown
#Unbleed the wounds for all the pain you endure
Give it back with interest, doesn't have to be a slur
#Undeserving plastic people with no soul
Spend time wisely, and you are a natural
#Uninspiring are the days without naughty thought

Bring out the creative child in you, it's never forgot
#Unhide the persistent choice of being embarrassed
You deserve more than you choose to be, uncurbed
#Unprecedented times in life does create vacuum
Bring your inner essence and create a new dream
#Unconditionally love everyone around you
But do you know, you deserve a better YOU?

by Arthi P

11

Empowered Women Empower Women

by Suhas Ramegowda

Empowerment happens when one gets a hold of the reins - either with some external support or by self-drive. For Sunita Suhas, although she had the support, she had to find the path to empowerment herself.

Typical Urbanite

Sunita Suhas led a typical urban lifestyle chasing materialist dreams in the corporate world. She then found a partner who also was part of this 9-5, Mon-Fri existence. She got married and soon had a baby - yay!

A typical urban Indian dream is fulfilled - a nice house, a baby, a dog for the baby, a garden, and a nice car. The husband was busy building his career so needless to say was inaccessible on weekdays and dead tired on weekends. Sunita had taken a sabbatical from her corporate life to stay at home and nurture her newborn. Husband not having the time meant she had to take a step back and attend to her baby which also meant she had to give her career a pass.

She never was a big fan of the corporate world so she didn't miss it much - she was in there because she had to work so that she could earn enough to pay her bills and fuel her lifestyle. But this 'stay at home' phase made her feel like a vegetable. She wanted to do more with her life - not that she thought playing a 'stay at home' role was menial. She believed she could do more while still managing her household. She also had the support of her husband, but she still had to figure out the path - what did she want to do?

Finding the 'maker' in her

Sunita always had a creative bent and more particularly, had an interest in textile. So once her boy grew old enough to start attending nursery, she made use of this time to up-skill herself in the world of textile. She signed up for a starter training and started from scratch - cutting, sewing, using the machine, etc. She had access to the internet so again, she made use of this access and dived into the world wide web feeding on everything related to the textile world. She took a liking to quilting so she started teaching herself the art of patchwork quilting. It wasn't easy particularly because she didn't have anyone guiding her personally. She was entirely dependent on the virtual community of quilters who mostly operated from outside of the country. After months of practising and honing her skill, she handcrafted her first patchwork quilt which she casually put-upon her personal social media account, and alas, it was sold in 20 mins. This gave her the idea that this newly acquired skill can be monetised. But she knew nothing about selling. So, whilst continuing to hone her quilting skills, she had to start from scratch on the art of selling. It didn't perturb her as she saw this too was a learning opportunity. She started off with Social media as a channel, so created a business page for herself on Facebook and got going. Every piece she made; it would instantly get picked up on Facebook.

Empowering other women

Now she knew how to make a product and how to sell too - but it still seemed incomplete. She realised that what she has painstakingly learnt needed to be shared - she now started to see her purpose. She wanted to empower more women with this art of quilting. She found her first student in her domestic help and soon she had other domestic help from the locality coming to her to learn this skill. They simply wanted to be empowered towards better living and they saw this art of quilting as a medium. This experience of imparting skill to other women and empowering them to a better living brought immense joy to Sunita and thus, brought more clarity to her onward path.

Although she didn't know what the immediate steps were, she knew deep inside that she no longer wanted to continue to live in a box, shackled by the limitations of an urban lifestyle. She also wanted a more meaningful life for her family. She wanted conditioning-free growing up years for her son. Apart from being a guiding light to the small group of women she was supporting, she also was looking out as a wife and a mother.

Un-schooling

Sunita chose to 'unschool' her son which meant he didn't go to a conventional school nor did he follow a set curriculum at home. He led his learning based on his interest areas. This approach provided him with holistic learning. This experience then inspired Sunita to take this 'unschooling' approach to the next level. She along with her husband decided to take a break from their respective commitments and along with their son decided to embark on an all-India road trip in their family sedan. The trip was largely un-planned which meant they had no bookings along the way.

They stayed with friends, did couch surfing, walked into hotels without a booking upon reaching a town/city along the way, etc. Most of this trip was amongst rural India and they covered around 11,000 km across 14 states in India over 60 days. These 2 months opened up her mind further and this was another step closer to her onward path.

Once back from this trip, Sunita started mulling over the big decision - to wrap up life in the city and move to rural India. She believed that rural India is where empowering needs to happen and rural India is where there is a better quality of life.

Big Decision

Mid-2017, Sunita along with her husband and son decided to wrap up their lives in the city. Husband quit his job with an oil gas major, son was already pursuing his unschooling journey so no real change for him except for a change in the environment. This decision didn't happen overnight. The whole family switched to minimalist living while still in the city - not eating out, doing all the household chores themselves, washing their vehicles themselves, buying only what they need, etc. They did this for a year before finally making the decision. They sold their entire household to the extent that they reduced their belongings to only 5 bags. They then spent a few months looking inward - learning Yoga and continuing to practice simple living. Sunita always had a thing for the mountains so they moved to the closest range - The Nilgiris.

Living amongst the wild

They drove to The Nilgiris with their 5 bags, checked into a hotel, and instantly started looking for a house on rent for a longer stay. They found one nestled in the woods in 2 days and thus began their life in the mountains. Sunita was also very keen on growing food so they bought a piece of land amidst the forest in a remote part of the mountains built an earth home with help of a few tribal people from a nearby village, cultivated the land to grow food, and lived amongst elephants, bears, leopards, wild gaurs, etc. in complete harmony. It was during this period that Sunita had a good time with the women from the nearby village and noticed that they were teeming with energy but didn't have the right platform to express it.

Birth of a Social entrepreneur

Sunita wanted to channel this energy to create something more meaningful for them and thus started Indian Yards, a social enterprise creating livelihood for women from rural and tribal communities. She started with 5 women - up-skilled them to be fine crafters of cotton fabric and designed functional and sustainable lifestyle products which she markets and sells across the globe. It wasn't easy, to begin with - a new land, new language, new culture but she found warmth among these women who grabbed this opportunity with both hands. She had to manoeuvre through a variety of emotions and expectations to earn their trust and commitment to the cause. Success is attractive so more women joined the group and there has been no looking back ever since.

Sunita has been running this enterprise for the last 2 years and currently supports around 30-50 women. Indian Yards currently handcrafts premium macrame products along with sustainable products for home, kitchen and lifestyle.

She believes there are a lot more women out there who need to be empowered and she's working towards making a larger impact. She is as excited, about the journey ahead, as she was when she taught her first student. You could keep a tab on her story by following her on Social Media –

Instagram - www.instagram.com/macrame.indianyards

Facebook - www.facebook.com/indianyards

12

From Prisdom To Queendom: A True Story Of A Mother's Longing And A Mother's Love

by Chantal Espitalier – Noel

The metallic doors of thirty meters height unbolted, slamming shut with a loud clanging sound. The warden's keys swinging at her wrist as I walked through. It's a place that none of us wants to be in. With a twist of a key, I'm locked in. Temporarily, I'm an animal trapped in a cage.

A sense of déjà vu takes over my being. Nature throws me into the cells of darkness, an endless war between Lucifer and the Angel Gabriel. Women punished cruelly by default, some entangled in the spider's web of drug trafficking, or petty offences, paying their dues to the laws of the land and the laws of karma.

As a life coach, it had become routine, and I was now immune to the milieu. As the gates closed behind me, the women smiled at me in comradery. Music classes playing loud, love songs bouncing back to my ears, all honouring their spirit and contribution to the human experience. Some begging hearts whispering to me to post a hidden love letter, addicts clinging to their daily dose, giving away their power to despair.

And for some, the cell had become the oasis that allowed them to escape, escape through the labyrinth of their imagination and cremation of their minds.

Anju, a thirty-year-old Mauritian woman, with full breasts and a zest for life, counted her remaining days, longing and dreaming to be free, free, and unshackled.

"This cell is my castle until I reach home," she said happily.

If nobody else could see it, perhaps destiny knew, Anju was made for greatness. Not only was she about to leave this castle behind, soon she would become a Queen.

After her release from prison, one night, out of desperation, Anju cried for help by dialling my number. Howling while describing the developing embryo within her body. We went through a roller coaster ride of all different options, starting from the absorption of the myriad of emotions to abortion and adoption.

As we said our goodbyes and I hung up the phone, the very next minute Marie called. A warm and loving friend living in the south of France, more precisely in the posh area of St. Remy de Provence. A place of celebrities and renowned artists, even Van Gogh.

Marie, distraught with her difficulties of conceiving a baby, let out a prayer to the universe, "All I want is to be a mother and I will open my heart to the one the Universe says is my child," cried Marie, in a hopeful tone.

Her words rang in my ears! I wondered in disbelief if she could have somehow magically eavesdropped into my previous conversation with Anju. It just wasn't possible. Was this destiny?

Marie had been spending her annual holidays in Mauritius for the last 10 years. She felt a deep connection with the local people and the island. She explained, the laws of adoption in Europe were tough and the waiting list very long with no guarantee. Marie, was a wealthy lady, stable, blessed with a flourishing business and only pregnant with words.

Anju, on the other hand, was already a mother of two children, in the middle of a divorce, penniless, jobless and with a sad prison history. She quickly concluded that she could not give this baby the life it deserved.

What were the odds of something like this happening within a minute of each other? Were they always meant to be? I was humbled to have been chosen as a medium for this divine union and arranged for Anju and Marie to finally meet. A loving and trustworthy relationship grew between both mothers.

I took care of Anju and took her to all the doctor's visits for the next seven months. All her medical care was paid for by Marie. The baby was healthy and growing well.

Before Anju knew his name, before she saw his face, before she counted his fingers and toes, she loved the baby that was inside her belly. She would often wonder if he'd look like her. She felt him move and said it felt like butterflies were fluttering in her belly. Then she felt his tiny little hands and his precious rounded knee pushing and twisting, and no one could see. It was their little secret.

The anxiety and joy were building up; Anju hoped and prayed that he would forgive her for not raising him. She loved her baby boy deeply and the adoption was an act of generosity, out of her deep love for him, for a better life and future.

The screaming pain on a Sunday, hailing a taxi, both mothers rushed to hospital. A beautiful baby boy named Léo was born in Mauritius on August 1st, 2011. The legal adoption was pronounced on the 11-11- 2011 at exactly 11 o'clock. The coincidence of the numbers was a clear sign of their destiny.

A precious gift bequeathed to them, from heaven above. Both mothers felt they had earned their rank and won the lottery. Adopting one child, may not change the world, but for that one child the world will change.

And what of Marie, Anju, and the baby? Marie honoured Anju as the divine mother. That bond was never broken. Léo is now nine years old, and lives the life of a little prince in St Remy de Provence with his loving adoptive family. He speaks to Mammy Anju on a weekly basis, and spends his holidays in Mauritius with her every year.

Two worlds collided and amongst shattered dreams and nature's broken promises, a picture of blood reunited. A woman once shackled and bound by the burden of the choices she had made, redeemed in the eye of her higher self. Anju walked away from Prisondom into Queendom. Her selfless act of a mother's love without attachment had made her a Queen.

13

Some Dreams

by Deepa Ragunathan

Malini sat on her veranda, waiting for her daughter to return home. Even as her eyes roved over the pages of the weekly magazine, her ears zoned in the tick-tocking of the giant grandfather clock, counting the seconds for her arrival.

"Malini! Tea!" Her husband of thirty years, Subhash, hollered for her from somewhere inside the house.

Sighing, Malini was tempted to ask him to make it himself, but with age came restraint. Raising to her feet, she dropped the magazine on the chair she got out of, and with one long glance towards the road, she made her way to the kitchen.

Her hands worked with years of experience, and she smiled as she remembered the days when she would struggle to light the stove. Subhash would shake his head in bemusement, before taking over the task.

"Malini! Come here!" Subhash's voice broke through the silent house, a summon.

She grumbled irritably. It used to be Linnie, and he used to ask her so politely to come. 'Can you come here, Linnie?' Somewhere along the way, that had vanished.

She bustled out of the neat kitchen, tea in hand, along with a tray full of biscuits. Making her way to his old office, she made a mental note to clean the house again, noting the gathering dust with distaste.

"What took you so long? I needed you to get me my phone." He didn't look up, his eyes focused on some ratty book.

Silently, she cleared a space on the table and left the tray there, before walking over to the shelf to get his phone.

"Listen, Malini... do you think we should start looking for a match for our daughter? She has grown up so fast." He began talking, taking a sip of his tea.

She brightened.

"I completely agree! Why, just yesterday, our neighbour's brother-in-law's son-" she spoke, only to be interrupted.

"My mother just called me about it. She met this family. Perfect match. The boy works abroad, but he is very cultured. They want an educated daughter-in-law, someone who can support them. Not one of those working women, but Subhadra can always quit her job." He said, eyes on his tea.

Malini sighed internally. Of course, he had already decided. Asking her was merely a formality.

She nodded softly, reaching for his empty glass. She got up, sighing loudly, and began to walk away when he spoke again.

"Come on, Malini, you don't agree with my choice. Do you have anything better?" He challenged, switching to English, eyeing her like he would look at his colleagues during a meeting.

How can I when you have only just told me? She wanted to scream at him, but she knew better. With age, she had gained restraint.

Instead, she simply said, “She has worked very hard for this job. She is going to get a promotion soon and asking her to give that up... it just doesn’t seem right. Would you give something like that up?” She added that last sentence as an afterthought, prompted by a rare thrust of courage.

His eyes narrowed.

“Yes, well, I don’t have to.” He said quickly, hands clenched.

She sighed.

“Maybe she doesn’t have to, either. Why can’t we look for another boy, someone who doesn’t mind her being employed?” She suggested tiredly, walking away from the silence.

That night, as she laid next to her rigid husband, she kept thinking about his words. *Yes, well, I don’t have to.* He truly believed that. He loved his daughter, cherished her every moment like a doting father should, but it was drilled into him for far too long that only women should compromise their desires and whims. It was generations of such thinking, against which paternal love hardly stood a chance.

It hadn’t been like this for her. She had never dreamed of a corporate job, and her parents, still old-fashioned to this day, had always told her that she was expected to be the perfect wife, and nothing more or less. But that hadn’t been the case for Subhadra. For all his faults, Subhash had always encouraged her to learn more, to achieve more, and to explore more. Is that why this turn of events stung so much?

Because it seemed crueller to show the world to a girl, and then snatch it away.

For a moment, she thought of the day her marriage was fixed. Was this how her mother had felt, back when they had told her that the match was fixed, and it was time to take her out of college? Had she also felt this pain, knowing that her daughter will always resent her for ending her education prematurely?

The bed shifted as her husband turned around to face her, wide awake.

"Is this what it was like for you, when you had to marry me?" He asked her, voice tortured, face twisted into a grimace. "I never thought much about how much you had given up because you had always smiled through it all."

She simply nodded, and for the first time in all her years of marriage, she felt her burden lighten.

"Why did you not say something? I never even realised that I was stealing your dream. I would never have wanted that!" He confessed awkwardly.

She smiled gently, leaning into him.

"It doesn't matter. I suppose I never really fought for them as our daughter does for hers. And I suppose you did give me a new dream after we married: our daughter. And she is everything we ever dreamed of! Let's just try not to kill her dreams, shall we?" She asked him earnestly.

He nodded, and they smiled, united for the first time since they were together, determined to make it a better world for their daughter.

14

Mukti

by Sitara Kumbale

Mukti was getting married tomorrow.

Mukti hadn't been able to sleep a wink. Next to her, her mother and the other ladies of the house snored away. She needed to step away from all the madness for a second and just breathe for a bit. The universe seemed to agree with her because that very second, a gust of wind knocked at the door and it opened with a slight creak. She stepped out of the room of sleeping women into the main hall. The main hall opened onto a wide stage with a shiny golden *mantap* adorned with orange and white flowers - a *mantap* where she was to sit and commit herself to a man ten years older than her.

As Mukti walked away from the *mantap* into the cool welcoming night, her mind flashed back to the night her father had told her she was getting married. It had been just after the festival of lights, *Diwali*. She was helping her mother clear away the lamps they had used for the *puja*. Both of them were sitting in the *puja* room, wiping the lamps of soot and oil remnants when her father walked in with a smile on his face and declared that she was to be married. He had arranged it all with the Shuklas and they had agreed that they were ready to accept Mukti into the family even though she was a little too old at twenty-two. Her mother had jumped up in joy and ran to whip up some sweets to celebrate the happy news.

However, Mukti hadn't been as thrilled. She was the educated one in their village. She had gone to school and had even graduated with a diploma in stitching and tailoring. Mukti had a dream; she wanted to move to Mumbai and make fashionable clothes. She'd seen actors on the television wear fashionable clothes, and she'd marvel at the designs hoping that someday her clothes would be seen on those actors. But with her father's declaration, her dreams had been shattered. She knew her family would never accept her dreams even if she were to tell them, especially her father. They were very conservative and all they cared about was their reputation and Mukti marrying into the Shukla family would improve their standing in the village. She had cried herself to sleep that night.

The months leading to the marriage had been nothing but torture for Mukti. She had to put on a smile and giggle as the aunties teased her about marrying such an 'eligible' man; she had to pretend that she was excited to pick out *saris* and jewellery for the marriage when all she wanted to do was scream - scream that she wasn't ready to get married, that she had dreams and goals she wanted to achieve and that marrying a man ten years older than her would turn her into her husband's baby-making machine and his family's servant. But she held her tongue and continued to smile, dying a little inside each day.

Mukti leaned against the parapet of the stairs leading to the main hall. What was she going to do? She wasn't ready to be married but if she didn't do anything, she'd be Mrs.

Gaurav Shukla in the next twelve hours. She needed to do something. She couldn't just sit there and do nothing as her dreams crashed and burned around her. She looked at the stars twinkling in the night sky and a lone tear escaped. She felt utterly alone and helpless. She couldn't confide in anyone or seek out anyone's help. Suddenly, a wild thought struck her mind. She could run away! She'd seen it happen twice before - the bride running away, but they'd always been found and married to their betrothed. They'd not been smart; they'd tried to hide away in the neighbouring villages but Mukti was smarter. She could go to Bombay and live her dream. She hesitated for a second. Her running away would hurt her family. It would seriously destroy their reputation. They may be even asked to leave the village. If Mukti left, she would never be able to come back to the village again. She would be ostracized by the community.

Mukti took a deep breath. She was stuck between a rock and a hard place. She could run away and maybe live her dream, but she'd never been able to see her parents again or she could get married and be unhappy for the rest of her life. It was a difficult choice to make but one she had to make soon. It would be dawn in an hour and people would begin to wake. She'd have no chance of getting away then. She stared hard at the night sky. It seemed to beckon her forth into the world, begging her to go out and seek what she pleased - to live out her destiny. She turned around and saw a wedding board. 'Mukti weds Gaurav', it said. She took another deep breath. She had made up her mind.

The next hour was a blur. She tiptoed back into the room of sleeping women and rapidly packed some jewellery and money into a bag filled with her clothes. She knew she had to be quick. The *Rajdhani* would leave the train station in thirty minutes and if she boarded it, they'd never find her. She walked the three kilometres to the station as fast as she could, lugging her bag along. The man at the ticket counter gave her a strange look when she asked for a ticket to Bombay. She didn't realize until much later that it was probably her *chuda* and sari.

Mukti didn't remember much of the train ride but she clearly remembered getting off the train and taking a deep breath. The air smelt of cigarettes, tea, and sewage. On the platform, somebody was playing a song from one of Shah Rukh Khan's old movies. She was in Bombay.

Mukti wasn't getting married tomorrow after all.

15

When Life Throws You A Rainy Day, Play In The Puddles

by Sumati Mohan

You perform best when you are unprepared. The innocence is your armour and the unknown path ahead is traversed with a certain high which only youth can count on.

Now that I have set the stage here comes a preview of my roller coaster ride through marriage, motherhood with a very interesting career. Juggling is an art that I learnt as a young girl of high aspirations and ambitions. That skill came in handy during my initial years of getting organized in an arranged marriage, joint family adventures, and managing a career. This was beautifully laced with spiritual quests. I had crashed landed on the fun ride in the initial months of my marriage. It ended when I got pregnant and was put on bed rest by my gynaecologist. Motorcycle riders on the streets of Bengaluru had to be stalled, trips to Mom's town was out of the question, dinner and lunch meetings with my husband's friends got postponed indefinitely, escapades to our spiritual master's ashram was not to be considered, late-night movie binging was to be replaced by reading magazines, aimless walks on the MG Road boulevard was not be dreamt of at all.

Was this the only stuff that I will be missing on or are there any other guesses? Remember I mentioned that I was this young girl, obviously back then, who had high aspirations and ambitions. I had to unceremoniously exit from my first organization. There was no room for a pregnant lady to continue to deliver her professional commitments, especially in a sales role.

Now I roll back to my former statement, you perform the best when you are unprepared, and the innocence is your amour. With the excitement of becoming a mother, critical health conditions, and with no idea of how things will unfold, the younger me still went ahead and made the biggest bet, I enrolled in a technical certification course. I invested my entire savings and plunged into the Information Technology industry.

The stay-at-home phase had its charm and anxious moments. The phase enlightened me on the joint family nitty-gritties. First, I learnt that it is best to live with a family. There's always someone who'll take care of you during a crisis. Secondly, finances are always a bone of contention, so keep one stream of income that is not joint family dependent. The third most important learning was to understand the traditions of the family so that you can carry the baton forward. Fourth, I realized that I cannot afford to take chances with my health. Voila! That became the bedrock principle of my life as I geared up for my Avatar 2.0.

The beautiful and pretty daughter arrived as destined, and the princess paved the way for a more determined me. The princess twirled, smiled, grinned, and charmed her way through our hearts. The tiny tot's beautiful face gave me the zeal to bounce back into life post the maternity sabbatical.

Maternity breaks were not cool back then. I did not want to end up in the teaching profession as I had no passion for it at all. The challenge now was where to apply and which stream to pick. What worked in my favour was that I had 4 years of work experience before my career break, had a Management degree in hand and while I took bed rest had also completed a few technical certifications. So, armed with all this I marched ahead to create a world that I had dreamt of. The process to achieve was unknown to me but what I had was a very strong determination, a family who wanted me to achieve my fullest potential, and the world full of possibilities waiting for me to explore.

So, I did not become the warrior queen and bundled my princess to the workplace, instead as a child always does, took the support of my Mom to help me raise my baby, while I geared up for staging a comeback in my career. Now, this might sound ruthless to a few but practical to some others.

I was part of the second category, the one who believed that one should reach out for help and seek assistance when there is a necessity and who could help you better than your Mom who has seen you through moments of joy, exhilaration, and jubilance.

The world was not waiting for me. Rather, I was the one seeking it. It was obvious, there was no red carpet laid out for me. Visits to recruitment firms, applications to organizations, screening online job openings, all became the norm of the day. There were offers but none of my interest. So, the practical me took up a lecturer position in a new management institute. I am sure you might be wondering; did she not just mention that she was not passionate about teaching. Correct, this was like a backup plan to keep me in touch with my subject, get me back to rhythm and ensure my cash flows outside of the joint family accounts. I always pat my back for being realistic in approach and if you are my kind of person, then you would also appreciate this particular skill of mine.

With the wheels on my skating rolls, I cruised through all the crisscross roads, slopes, and heights, crest, and trough, bumps, and bends. This was a phase where I was working hard and extremely focused, there was no room for lethargy nor complacency, but there was ample room for new opportunities, and I was almost starting from scratch. Was it tough, hmmm, now, I was only driven by incremental benefits, so any small victory would appear big to me.

Well, as I had mentioned earlier there were troughs, bends, and slopes that I had to negotiate to keep marching ahead in my life, and in that context, I would like to narrate one particular incident which temporarily put me in a self-doubt mode. One of the leading Banks was recruiting management-level executives. I appeared for my written exams, group discussions, interviews, and was in the top 10 shortlisted. They had 5 openings and my final round was with senior panellists. The senior panellist was excited to see the only profile of MBA with Marketing & Finance major in the top 10 shortlists. I was asked if I can relocate to a small town in Karnataka. The no barred me jumped to the opportunity and said yes. But then came the actual twist – "As a young mother how will you manage to work in a remote location?" promptly asked the panellist. I knew with this query thrown in; the deal will not be sealed. This was one of the setbacks that I faced as a young mother wanting to stage a comeback in the corporate world.

There were several victorious moments, and I cherry-picked those great opportunities that came my way and moved on. Since then I have had a stellar career of managing varied portfolios with MNCs at various India based and international locations. Smaller setbacks can be converted into a meaningful prospect based on how you choose to react.

I witnessed life through a prism and my actions translated into a multi-coloured life. While the princess was growing up beautifully and I was juggling the household responsibilities and work. Somewhere along this path, I managed to make my life not only about work and home but also about overall wellbeing.

I squeezed time for regular walks, yoga asanas, and meditation and embedded it seamlessly as part of my overall routine. I also travelled extensively on leisure and for work. Travelling is quite therapeutic, and it opened up my mind to larger dimensions of life with exposure to various cultures and traditions. It's not that I imbibed them all, but such exploration broadened my perspective.

One thing where I steered away from is being involved in any capacity in my husband's business. He continued to make that offer, but smarter me ensured that apart from being a life partner, I will not collaborate with him on any such initiative. This decision of mine, really helped me to look at his work objectively and wear a consultant's hat to provide review inputs whenever necessary. A second obvious benefit is that we remained good friends more than business partners. This decision brought in a certain calmness in our relationship, and we stayed committed to whatever we were interested in, without getting too involved in each other's work.

Life moved on with its highs and lows, and I kept matching the pace of life and kept dancing to her rhythm with the enthusiasm of a young girl. Did some very outrageous stuff by challenging the status quo of joint families in terms of decision making for the family business and managed the whole process through skilful negotiation with elders to drive acceptable agreement for all the stakeholders involved. Pulled off an Electric Car driving on the busy roads of Bengaluru with the skill of navigating a scooty. Another role that I donned was driving service activities for CSRs and NGOs. This stint gave me exposure to the other side of the world, primarily the ones who needed attention and assistance.

Managing joint family responsibilities, professional commitments, raising a young girl (of course with the help of my parents), passionately involved in my interests, I never lost sight of having a good sense of humour and could laugh loudly on all my failures or attempts which didn't yield the desired results.

At this juncture in my life, I am collaborating with my husband as a strategist to set up his new venture, fine-tuning my daughter's approach towards studies & freelancing projects, involved in few service initiatives, and of course, I still have a very strong career ahead of me. My mantra – Make mistakes but learn from them very quickly and then again make a few new mistakes, but never stop trying. Do have realistic expectations out of life, stay focused, be young at heart and you will achieve what you set out to achieve.

16

The Good-Girl Obsession

by Nirosha Tomy

"You're such a good girl," they said with a hand on my head and a pat on my shoulder, as I stood there with a twinkle in my eyes and an ear-to-ear grin. Yes, I was a good girl! The little me, only 5, prided myself in being a good girl. As I grew older, trying to live up to the ladylike behaviour that society dictated, this compliment became a part of my being. But little did I know that these words, that were honey to my ear were my Achilles' heel, incarcerating me within the bars of societal hypocrisies. A "good girl" would never talk loudly, argue, disobey, disregard authority, neglect her duties, or overlook others' opinions. This is exactly what Sophocles meant when he said, "silence is an ornament for women" and "a good girl should be seen, not heard". Simple right! But the devil lies in details that are never said out loud, the ones that must be inferred by reading between the lines, the ones that stereotype women and their role in society to be a man's property.

They say to teach them young as it's easier to uproot a sapling than to chop off a tree. The notion of a good girl is such an attempt made by the patriarchal society, which could not bear women standing up to men at an equal footing. The obstinacy in ensuring the upbringing of girls as "good" has led to the name-calling of those who stray from these set norms. This is why we try our hardest to maintain that good girl image. Without realizing any of this, here I was trying diligently to keep up my good girl branding, to maintain a perfect image of a self that wasn't me, to please everyone around me, and to rise to the conventional and often rigid standards set by the society. And my Dunkirk spirit, to meet these unattainable standards regularized through societal norms and values broke me.

At the age of 15, I found myself standing at a crossroad in life considering permanent escape from my hell. Without realizing it I had developed the 'good girl syndrome' which further triggered my anxiety and depression, failing to maintain my false image curated to meet the societal norms. Ironically, what pushed me to the edge pulled me up and my plan did not follow through as it dawned on me that if my attempt failed, I would have to deal with what society would think of me. At that moment I decided that no matter what, I'm not going back to that rabbit hole again. Listening to this one might think I changed, like a phoenix rising from the ashes of my past and soaring high above the societal norms. I finally broke through the traditions that bound my wings. With newfound confidence, I pursued my dreams. I let my creativity run wild, painting rainbows of a fresh canvas. I was finally free. If this is what you came for, I'm sorry I have let you down. Now you may join the esteemed panel of idealistic critics, who would be reading this with a stern look on their face hoping their children turn out to be better than me.

No, I did not change much. I did not come out of my state of despair, I did not suddenly become rebellious, and I did not make decisions based on my happiness. I did not defy my parents, nor did I speak what was on my mind. No, and no and no to all that you thought happened between the time I came down from that ledge to now as I write this. I believe that such a drastic change is only possible if a miracle occurs, and such a miracle did not happen in my case. The 'one moment of breakdown giving rise to a strong-willed, independent, successful person', turning a new leaf is a notion popularized by fairy tales and movies and it is not to be blamed for it as they provide hope to innocent people at the most trying times. But for people like me, who hit rock bottom, end up drunk with sorrow, crying over every song on the playlist be it happy or sad, for us these fairy tales and movies are sources of further regret and despair, which is totally beside the point. Life is no movie and there are no superheroes to come save you as you fall from the grace of society. In life, you have to be your hero, or your villain and I love my villains more.

So, I go on every day dealing with the demons inside my head, afraid of losing control and letting the darkness overrule all light in my life. I may seem weak to some, irrational to others, and stubborn to most for sticking to the values and education I was raised in as a child. These values and education are products of patriarchy but I'm going to live with it. I continue hustling; working hard to remain the good girl that I was meant to be, believing that someday I'll be at a better place in life. I do what I'm expected to do, consolidating my position as a villain in my life. This may seem anti-climactic to all my dear readers who find the death of a hero unjustifiable. As unfair as it may seem, sometimes in life, you find solace in the very thing that caused you grief. It is my choice to avoid change and I blame no one for it but once in a while, I wonder how my life would be if I had a different upbringing. I wonder what would have entailed if I had made different choices, had I made that jump. And now and then, to the waning moon, I tell a heart-warming story of a girl who could never be a good girl, a girl who was never me.

17

Footsteps Covered

by Dr. R. Uma Sharma

In the town of Tadipalem there once lived a couple, Sastry and Lakshmmma, in a two-floored building on a small street. They had three daughters and four sons. The youngest of them was Gouri. She was a cute and active girl with a lot of enthusiasm. She was as wise as Lord Shiva's wife Gouri. From childhood, Gouri was a restless girl with a lot of ambition. The family lived a frugal life due to their economic situation. As the youngest kid, she was always showered a bit more love than her siblings. She was the only one whose birthday was celebrated. Her mother would feel ecstatic when little Gouri would sing rhymes in English, and even considered such acts as an achievement. She used to proudly speak of her daughter's recitation skills to all the neighbours.

Time changes a lot of things. Every moment and every day brings new hope in us. As Gouri reached puberty, she was able to understand the circumstances at home and school. At school, she witnessed that her economic background always affected the relationships with her friends and classmates. Being a part of a middle-class family is enough to teach an adolescent many life lessons. All her elder brothers got jobs and settled in different places. The elder sisters got married and moved to their in-law's houses. Gouri was then the only child who lived with her parents. She had to discharge the role of a daughter and a son as well. She always yearned to watch movies in theatres, going to picnics with her classmates, but she could not because of her family's financial conditions. She was also slightly attracted to one of her classmates. He used to follow her every day from her house to college. She never dared even smile at him, because she did not want to complicate her life or her parents' lives. She would just concentrate on her academics, typing classes as well as housework.

As an adolescent girl, she always believed her life was completely in her control. But sometimes, in life, strange things happen. She always wanted to become a Doctor, but because of her father's economic conditions, she decided that she would at least become a nurse. She strongly thought that being a nurse is the best way to serve society. Unfortunately, in her hometown, there was no science graduation course to study. Her father could not send her out of town for graduation as it was a financial burden for him. She had only two options in life, to continue with the courses in her hometown or to quit education completely and stay at home. But Gouri was determined not to quit her education at any cost. She decided to go where life took her. She continued with arts in her graduation. She studied on her own and prepared her notes. She studied hard and was awarded the topper of the college award. "Life becomes peaceful when you accept life as it comes." She was enjoying every 'Ichigo Ichi' moment in her life. (Japanese term for 'living the moment').

Gouri's mother decided that they could not send her for higher education and decided to get her married by finding a suitable alliance for her. Gouri's mother had already decided on the groom for Gouri. It felt as if time flew. Gouri got married as soon as she graduated with an arts degree and went to Bangalore, the state capital of Karnataka. She was just a naive innocent girl, born and brought up in a small town. She did not have any prior exposure to a big city like Bangalore. She did not know a single word of Kannada, the language that people in Karnataka spoke.

Every step and each moment became a lesson for Gouri. Her father-in-law arranged a reception for his city friends. She had never witnessed a single reception in her small town. She did not know how to stand or how to present herself on the stage. Her body language was stiff, and it was witnessed by the audience. It was then that Gouri understood that her graduation, her skills, or her class topper position are not enough to survive in this city. She realised that she is just a nursery student, who had to learn many things from that day.

New life, new environment, a new language, the new things that surrounded Gouri forced her to be more proactive and to learn from every moment. She used to feel insecure when all the family members spoke in Kannada. She was so curious to learn and understand those words and started learning from small children and cart vendors. She would observe every dialogue in the shows telecasted on television.

The newly-wed couple was happy for some days. Life was like a flowing river. Her husband started going to the office, her father-in-law and her brother-in-law all went to their jobs. Getting up early, doing all household duties, preparing lunch boxes for everyone, washing clothes, going to the temple with her mother-in-law, and coming back with vegetables and arranging, preparing things throughout the day became a daily routine for Gouri. Every evening, she would get ready and wait for her husband to take her somewhere.

Years passed by, Gouri became a mother of two children, one boy, and one girl. She lost her enthusiasm and dreams for a few years and started working like a robot. Her children too added to her duties list, she started packing lunch boxes for them too. Sometimes she used to recollect her past and she used to compare it with her present life. She understood that her life is only now surrounded by doing household works and discharging duties for family members. She understood the importance of economic freedom, which makes a person self-sufficient.

Gouri's favourite subject History taught her that many mistakes done by other people could also be life lessons for us. She started thinking of new dimensions about how she could change her lifestyle and how she wanted to lead her life. No person on this earth is a skill-less person. Every person is abundant in some or other life skills. She acknowledged and accepted her current situation and set sail to change the course of her life.

There is absolutely no age for learning. Gouri came from a teacher family and she used to teach small children. She started introspecting about her skills and how she wanted to grow as a person. Introspection or positive self-talk has the power to take anyone in the right direction of life. She understood there is a lot to learn to survive in the city and to work. She realised the importance of learning Kannada and English to survive in Bangalore. She started going to Kannada class and started speaking with the surrounding people.

She realised that "English" is the key to get her career unlocked. The first step towards solving a problem is to recognise there is one. Gauri realised that she wasn't very fluent in communicating in the English language and wanted to work upon that.

All these thoughts about shaping her life and starting a career started pounding upon her only after she realised that financial stability is paramount. With all that in mind, she made her first move to work on her communication skills. But on the other side of the balance was her family which was the important part for her. She had to think of a way to work on her skills without causing a disturbance in her family. She did not want to override her duties in the family. Finally, she was able to figure out the perfect algorithm which worked the best for this.

She enrolled herself in an English-speaking class and made sure that the timings would not clash with any of her household duties. This helped her to see a bigger picture of what mattered to be professional at something. Soon she realised that being only a graduate would not help her climb the ladder. She would not get promoted until she was more qualified and experienced. Living in a city like Bangalore turned out to be advantageous for her. A metropolitan city has way more diverse opportunities for vivid types of career requirements. Amidst all this river of thoughts in her mind, her biggest background aim was to earn money and at the same time pursue a career in her passion for teaching.

Soon her kids were growing up and were independent enough to take care of themselves. That's when Gouri took a firm decision to kick start her career. This was the time when everyone's eyes were on her as she made her biggest move ever. She started small and landed her first job as a nursery school teacher. A half-day job helped her manage the conditions at home as well. Her first salary was a thousand rupees which were her biggest treasure. She had her proudest moments counting those 100-rupee notes enclosed in an envelope with her name on it. She was overwhelmed and bought gifts for all the family members with her first salary. That's it! From this day on, her career started taking shape. She started getting many more opportunities. Maybe the universe does support us if our dreams are pure, and our heart is in the right place. Soon she landed at a bigger school and was now a high school teacher.

Though she started making more money from her new job, she never left her passion for learning and continued to study side by side while working. As the years passed, the degrees next to her name kept increasing. She completed her post-graduation and then her M.Phil. Soon she was no more just Gauri but Dr. Gauri after she completed her Ph.D.

This gave her the required thrust to rocket herself and land jobs in the most prestigious institutions in Bangalore. She was now a professor handling the entire language department in these institutions. She turned out to be the person whom the students looked up to not just for their doubts from the textbook but also for their queries about life issues. She did not lose her focus and kept progressing in both her career as well as gaining skills.

In this delightful journey, she got opportunities to meet so many new people and these new friends have not only inspired her but have helped her grow into a better person. Each one of them has taught her something new which eventually made her life so much more colourful. It changed her perspective about a few things which helped her feel more motivated to try things outside her comfort zone.

Well, in this ever-changing universe, things turned out to be fruitful in her life. Today she is a very successful teacher who does not just teach lessons from a textbook but rather gives insights about greater things in life. She is a true motivator and guides students to choose a career path which they are passionate about. She is a role model for many of her colleagues and students.

Isn't it just amazing, when a girl from a small town does whatever it takes to turn her dreams into a reality? Isn't that the crux of any other movie these days? Her life was also no less than a movie. She started from the bottom and always wanted to reach the stars. The most important part here is to acknowledge her bravery and the way she tackled her obstacles along the path to success. She always wanted to lead in changing the way society perceives a few things.

She has always dreamed big and felt the need to broaden her reach. On this front, she started her YouTube channel named 'Coffee Baate' where she posts motivational videos every week.

Her consistency and her hard work have paid well and today she stands as an example to show everyone that dreaming big and doing whatever it takes to complete that is the only and the ultimate step toward turning them into reality. The most important part is to never forget the journey you took to reach your destination. Dr. Gauri's is still on her journey and is trying out newer paths to her destination. Stating Robert Frost here, from the poem Stopping by Woods on a snowy evening, "There are miles to go before I sleep...".

18

The Women I Want To Be

by Lakshmi Priyanga M.

Hi! I'm Saval. I am 28 years old, and I live with my family in Toronto, Canada. This is my story. To start with, I was lucky to have a childhood surrounded by a lovable family. But it was not the same for my parents. Oh, what can I say about my mother and her sisters! I'm truly blessed to be a part of their family. They are inseparable. My grandparents died at a very young age and my mom was just a year old at the time. I refer to my mother and her sisters as 'super sisters' and you might wonder why. We have heard many stories about what growing up without parents is like. It truly is a struggle. In my mother's story, there was no 'superhero' to support or guide them. All they had was each other and their determination to fight against their struggles. They never gave up despite having faced numerous struggles and various obstacles. My mother narrated her story to me and she said something that still rings in my ears to this day. She said, "Being women, the journey wasn't easy for us, but that didn't stop us from living. It shouldn't." I didn't understand what she meant at that time. She always made me believe that being a woman means being strong.

Now that I think about it, my journey starts here. I grew up in a joint family and it was a package in itself, with its pluses and minuses. Unlike some other families, my family wasn't orthodox or traditional. My father worked as an attorney with a law firm. He was hardworking but he wasn't a family man. He was such a workaholic that he prioritized his work over us, his family! I didn't get to spend a lot of time with my father, but I longed for it. The super sisters backed me up; they are my world. Since both my parents had a rough childhood, they made sure that I got everything I needed and protected me all the time. As a result, I became an over-protected dependent kid. I had people doing my work for me, be it small errands or significant tasks. Every aspect of my life was well planned, and I always had someone to back me up. I didn't have many friends; while other kids my age tried different things, I was at home spending time with my family. I am not complaining, but I did feel safe and comfortable throughout my childhood.

Despite all this, something was amiss. My classmates hesitated to talk to me. I didn't care much about their thoughts though, because I always had my mom, and she was my best friend. I completed high school and decided to pursue law in the same university where my father studied in India. Now, this was the first time I stepped out from my happy, comfortable life to a rough or rather an unknown path with no one to back me up. I wondered whether or not I'd even survive! I wouldn't have the super sisters being there for me all the time. I was alone. That's when reality hit hard. I was grateful for the comfortable life I had, but I had a feeling of emptiness in my life. I felt it even when I smiled and was happy with my family. I decided to find out what it was.

It was in this chapter of my life that I had a revelation. My time in college was a nightmare and I can't even think of where to begin! Being the overprotected, female child I was, I found it difficult to cope with everything, not just academics. I was very scared, and I had no social and communication skills. I didn't talk to anyone. I felt as though I was an outcast. I was enraged and upset. I thought to myself, "Why am I not able to live a normal life and hang out with my classmates? Why do I find it difficult? Is something wrong with me?" There were too many questions I had.

Being a student of law, I learned to think twice before making a decision. I didn't enjoy the first four years of my time at university. It was only during my final year that I took a step for myself and voiced my opinion. That made me understand something- being a woman doesn't mean you shouldn't enjoy life. Not everyone around you is there to hurt you. If you're expecting something to change, it's you who must take the first step. I still remember calling my mom and telling her that I wanted to quit and return home. But I had so much more to face in life! Imagine how lonely a young woman would feel, in a new, unknown place. My loneliness killed me, but I didn't want to upset my mother and I avoided thinking about it. During my low and rough patches, I found strength in my mother's words, "Tough times come and go, but we have to sail along." It made me think a lot about my future and where I was headed. That's when I realized that my mom and her sisters had always prioritized other's interests over their own. Even after marriage, my interests were a top priority, above theirs. I remember my mother wanting to become a radio jockey, but she didn't. She couldn't. Why couldn't she? These thoughts of mine lingered.

After graduation, when I returned to Canada, I felt like a different person. I questioned everything and this side of mine wasn't something my father welcomed.

The next chapter in my life was marriage. I believe my family was very serious about the concept of my marriage and they wanted me to get married and settle down early in life, by the time I was 23 years old. I had only just begun to step out into the world and explore life and now, my family wanted me to settle. I fought with them. I was against their decision, but they didn't understand me. I made a rash decision to leave the house. I disappointed my family, especially my mother and her super sisters.

Looking back, I should've stayed and made them understand my point, but that phase in my life taught me a lot. Just like my father, I worked very hard. I took control of my own life. I took several part-time jobs. There were times when I had to sleep on the streets. I saved money and rented out a small house. Finally, I landed a job after fulfilling several qualifications to become an attorney. I was placed in a temporary provincial position. I was a newbie and lots of work was piled on me. The male workers in my firm passed comments and even my boss mocked me once saying that being a woman in this field was difficult and that I would have to be flexible sometimes, with a smirk. I didn't understand what he meant by that.

One day, it was around 9 pm and everyone was wrapping up work for the day. A colleague informed us that there was an ice-breaking session for all the young advocates and interns. I tagged along and we entered some pub where women were forced to consume alcohol. I was forced by my seniors to have a glass. I felt tipsy and that's when things started going out of control. My boss tried to molest me and in that moment of shock, I rushed out of the pub immediately. I went home, but I couldn't get a hold of myself. I didn't know what happened there and why. I was a lawyer and my boss who tried to molest me was an attorney too.

I was confused about whether or not to confront him the next day. I remembered my mother's words again, "Being women, the journey wasn't easy for us, but that didn't stop us from living. It shouldn't" At that moment, I knew I had to confront him.

I walked straight up to my boss said, "You molested me! Who gave you the authority to do so?" He smirked again and told me to stop talking rubbish. He said I wanted it and called me names. I had to raise my voice and I filed a case against him. Now what? Did I resign from my job and leave the firm? No, I didn't. I stayed.

It wasn't easy but I didn't need to resign from my job because of someone else's mistake. I made a firm decision to stay right where I was. After I registered a complaint, many women from my office came forward and registered their complaints as well. I missed my family and I needed them. I went back to them and apologized. We reunited and I gained more strength. My family was very proud of me. It's been two years since that incident. I currently work as an attorney with the same firm, a position I earned on my own.

What I want to convey through my story is that we are women, and we are strong. I underwent a complete transformation. From being an overprotected kid without any social skills to the courageous, young, spirited, and independent woman I am, I carved my own life. I raised my voice. I am now happily married and this time around, it was my wish to do so. I have a child of my own. It has made me super powerful. Being a woman is powerful in itself. If you're a mother, trust me, you can rule the world! Being a woman, a girl, a lady or a trans-woman gives you that gutsy feeling. It's an inbuilt characteristic and it is there in every woman. You just have to acknowledge it. We can be the woman we want to be, and nothing can stop us. A lot of women have faced a lot more difficulties than I have. The only difference is that I raised my voice and fought till my voice was heard. It takes a fraction of a second for you to decide whether you want to be the woman of someone's dream or a woman of your dream. I'm grateful for everything that has happened thus far in my life. I cherish it all and I will continue to be the amazing woman that I am.

19

The Women Who Made Me

by Rakshita Nagaraj

We wage wars every day. With our bodies, our souls, and along with other women.

Growing up, I was constantly told to look a certain way, to behave a certain way, and learn skills that are going to benefit my 'family to be.' I was told to learn cooking, otherwise, who will feed my husband and kids? I was told that irrespective of the accomplishments, starting a family has to be prioritized. I was told a lot of things that satiated the patriarchal society. It took a lot of effort to unlearn this thought process. To break the shackles of patriarchy and lead a life of my choosing. It took hundreds of stories to make me the feminist I am today.

To begin with, I had huge issues with the way I looked. I had a lot of body image issues. To be honest, I definitely would like to point fingers at the numerous fashion magazines. Not one magazine showed me a woman who looked like me. Not one.

It took Kim Kardashian to break the internet which led me to realize that there are women out there who look curvy. It took Jamila Jamil to wage a war on the diet culture to help me realize that we need to strive to be healthy and our understanding of BMI changed overnight which pushed most of us out of the healthy category. I owe it to these women who helped me get comfortable with my body.

I was always told education is the top priority, but I have various interests and ambitions. A highly successful woman is never appreciated. I was told to be ambitious but not too ambitious. Marie Currie was the only woman who I had come across for a major portion of my life. It was not until I entered college and interacted with my female (sounds extremely absurd to use this prefix) professors to understand the contribution of women in science. They drove me to take up my Master's. Their implicit encouragement helped me develop a passion for research. The current Nobel winners, Jennifer Doudna, Emmanuelle Charpentier, and Andrea M Ghez, apart from their incredible contribution to science have inspired countless young girls to take up science.

When Michelle Obama said "when they go low, we go high" I can fathom the numerous young girls she has inspired. When AOC talks about the new bills she is going to introduce or when we look at Jacinda Ardern and her COVID-19 disaster response and management, it helps me realize that women belong everywhere where decisions are being made. When Beyoncé released the Lion King music video, it made me take pride in the culture that my body embodies.

The women/no binary folks on Instagram, the likes of Saloni Chopra, Dr. Trinetra, Alok V Menon, Dolly Singh, etc. helped me understand the nuances of sexuality.

The nitty-gritty of sexism. The importance of oneself. The importance of one's needs. The need to be unapologetically oneself. The need to stand up for what is right. These women have done more to help me mould my thoughts and make me the women I am today.

How can I forget the woman in my life? My friends, with their constant support and love. My mother, for the grit and patience she portrays. My sister reminds me every day to never lose the child in me. My domestic help who despite her lack of education, sends her children to school and encourages them to dream and have ambition.

As I said previously, we wage war on ourselves every day. But the women around me make it easier for me.

They made me the feminist I am today.

20

Engaged

by Amala L.

"What do you do?" I was asked. Damn. That was so awkward; not for being asked what I do, but for being a boy from an orthodox family, I was serving someone coffee in the pretext of getting introduced to my future life mate!

"Umm. B-school student. Undergraduate" I replied with my head down, being respectful.

The girl sat in the middle of the crowd, on the sofa sporting a formal black blazer. Her hair was tied into a tight bun at the top of her head. She was dusky-looking and she reminded me of a coffee bean. Her mom and dad were sitting adjacent to her. I assumed that she was to be the bride when I noticed her authoritative attitude through the side of my eyes.

"What's your name, by the way?" She asked me, sipping her coffee.

"Shiv," I said in a low voice, shyly. My dhoti was not tied tightly enough, thus not allowing me to stand up straight. So, I ran back to the corner of the kitchen. But the sound from the living room still searched my ears to convey what was going on.

"How much will you do, uncle?" She kept her legs on one another and was asking my old-aged dad. My mom's usual worrying face caught my sympathies.

"Mmm... Whatever you expect", my dad replied in hesitation.

"Good. I think we will leave for now and get back to you soon."

They got up from the sofa beside the huge teapoy of snacks, especially the bajji and suji, half-eaten like a squad of squirrels, leaving the place looking messy and haphazard. I peeped out to see my lady-to-be, and I still remember her gesture when she turned back to wave at me. She was so bold and strong which made me feel she could be my perfect half. My family thought the same, I hoped because no one ever bothered to ask for my opinion. While my thoughts were wandering around here and there, my eyes were still on her, as she drove out of the gate in her SUV. This feels amazing! Woah! She didn't even ask me if I could cook. I loved that- I meant her 'progressiveness'!

Ouch! I hit my leg! My body started to shake, and I began sweating profusely. I could find some cushions near me and my head was dizzy. I woke up with a jerk. 'Hell, is this all a nightmare?' I kept my hands on my forehead and searched for water near my bed. The room was horrifyingly dark, and my heartbeats were racing. I tried to reach my hands to the light switch and hit that on the other side. The night became even clearer. The long growl of the street dogs scared me. I tied to recall why I woke up suddenly, and what was that one dream that made me anxious. Oh my God! Wait. Is this all a dream? I went up to the washroom and splashed some fresh water on my face to cool my eyes. I wished that the water could travel inside my head, to make my brain feel cool too!

Who am I? The red bindi was flowing through my eyes like blood. The sarees along the hanger brought me back to the darkness of my 'realities'. I am Shiv. A 21-year-old business school student. I was been forced to get married by my family and welcome to my story of patriarchs and internalized misogynies. Oh! I forgot to add! I am a 'girl'.

Everyone asks me. "Why is your name Shiv? Isn't benchmarked for a boy?". But one doesn't know what is the most irritating thing they do after this question. A peal of idiotic laughter! I would be stuck there knowing what not to do. But more than me, my mother was asked this question many times. Mostly I was the one who did that to her.

"Why did you even name me like this?" I would ask getting annoyed.

"Because some things are meant to be". She would manage to reply while cleaning the dishes with a sigh.

There were days when I used to get trolled for my name a lot. I used to cry in washrooms. But times changed when I got proud of having a 'boyish' name.

But time has changed me again. I feel proud to be a woman now, and I seriously don't want a guy's name. But I need a guy's place in society. A place that is respected for who they are and not for who they want-to-be. I too want to be financially independent. I too want to get married at the age of 27 or 28. I too want to be asked whether I want that marriage. I too 'not' want someone to embarrass me with my dress! I too want to be a human! But the real question is, could it even be dreamt?

God, I again got lost seeing the Shiv, at the mirror whom I want to be. The dogs outside continued to make noise. I wish I could have at least been born like them.

I came out of the restroom with a white towel over my wet face, trying to erase the bindi. How come it defines me when my talent and brains couldn't!

I remember my mom telling me, before going to bed, "Tomorrow is a big day, beta" She patted on my shoulders and gave me a wide smile.

Yes. It's a big day for me and my family. It was my engagement. But I was not sure if I wanted to! My father is a businessman, and he was clear to give all his legacies including his leadership, only to my brother who is not interested. Whereas, he wanted me, who was a B-school student to get married and cook for my future husband. How strange! It was not that I didn't fight. Many a times, parents have resorted to emotional blackmail as a means of getting their children married. Such is mine too!

His name is Dev- my husband-to-be. I met him last week, in an exact scenario that struck my nightmares. The only difference was that- I was a girl. And he was a boy. But I wished I could be in his place wearing a black blazer and sipping up coffee. Sometimes a dream gets fulfilled at least when you sleep, right?! I was staring at the tick-tock clock, up against the pinkish wall. Who told you I would like pink? The architect was not aware, because he was just told that it was their daughter's room and he just splashed some pink on it. I grabbed a pillow chucked it against my chest. My heart was burdened. I rested against the couch and slept.

"THUD... THUD"

My mom was banging on the door the next morning.

"Shiv... What are you doing inside? Open the door. Its time. The groom's family are on their way"

Oops. I panicked and woke up from the couch falling. "Yeah ma. I am getting ready. Just give me five minutes"

"Open the door, let your sisters help you out."

"Five minutes."

I shouted and rushed to the washroom and got myself a quick shower for my body and brush my teeth simultaneously. The water droplets watered my pastedown on the brush making it soggy. YUCK.

I wrapped my saree in a hurry and hoped my ornaments would do some justice to it. My cousins were already shouting outside, and I could hear a coarse of exotic laughter from the aunties. I wonder how these ever 'moral policing' and 'traditional' aunties, all of a sudden, turn cheesy during marriages.

I opened the door and a dozen of my cousins were standing with bangles, ornaments, bindis, make-up kits, and whatnot. Everyone surrounded me making me up, laughing, and teasing. My usual black lips were turned red. My short hair was supported by long fake hair and was layered with a fresh thread of jasmines. My hands felt shackled with the heavily threaded bangles while my face experienced a new high of a model-like look with the perfect amalgamation of 7 shades of elegant compact powders. While there were making this perfect-girl image on me, I heard a little girl run towards my room and cried in joy at everyone, "The Groom has arrived!". Everyone started laughing and patting me on my shoulders. The grandmas come from nowhere and tell you something that you should smile for, with shyness and here came one and whispered into my ears, "You look so beautiful. Your life is going to start today. Be a perfect housewife and you will be happy." She pressed her hands against my head, and I tried not to freak out.

Finally, after 12 minutes of the same sorrow, I was called out as the priest had declared that it was time. There were nearly 65 members in our house. I was asked to sit near my parents and the groom's family was seated opposite to us, while the priest was the judge here, as he sat in the middle. I noticed huge whispers among the crowd after I arrived and there were also some hands pointing towards me.

The priest continued to chant and suddenly he called parents from both sides to exchange some plates to confirm the alliance. My parents got up and Dev's too. I noticed that Dev was looking at me and I started to feel uncomfortable.

His attitude suddenly got me to my senses. Wait. What am I even doing? Am I going to marry a stranger who is 7 years older than me? Am I going to go and live in his house and do all his chores for him, the rest of my life? Am I going to depend on him to have an identity of my own? Who is Shiv then? Being a girl, don't I require the freedom of creating my own identity? Being a girl, don't I have the responsibility of undertaking the family business? Being a girl, don't I have the duty of taking care of my parents?

I managed to look at my brother who was standing in a corner with a wide smile, because of the dispersal of one of his 'duties'-getting his sister married! Wait. Does he have answers to all my questions? Is it worth it because of the few lakhs that my parents were giving away as dowry? No. I can write my answer.

I got up. In a daring voice, with sharp eyes, I looked at Dev and said, "I don't want this wedding. Sorry for not being sorry". I chined up and threw the garland. A huge wave of shock and dismay rose in the crowd again, as the rumours and character assassination were already on their way! I turned to them, "It is for me. Myself. And my family" And looked at my puzzled parents with a knowing look and an assuring smile.

IN

RAPTURES

21

Seed of Life

Night was dark but bright enough to reflect
a beam of candle in four passionate eyes.
Aroma of sweat spread out
dampness inside the room.
The twinning shadow on the bedroom wall
faded away by the fuzzy fumes.
It was the same unforgettable night,
as a gift of his divine love,
your father dropped a seed of life
inside my womb.
There sprouted another heartbeat to
make me feel complete.
Awaited nine months of sleepless nights
caressed me with a whiff of nostalgia.
I was torn while wrestling with pain to
push that little life out of me.
The day I saw you born on a red blood carpet,
we met for the first time
like strangers; where again reflected
a spark of joy in four tearful eyes.

by Maria Mappilassery

22

A Hundred Mothers

How lucky am I ?
To have a hundred mothers
So many smiling faces
To shower me with love
And blessings and kindness
Great food in abundance
And the friends whom I cherish
Memories to reminisce
How lucky am I ?
To have seen such wonder
It's a question that comes to me often
As I sit down to think and ponder
How lucky am I ?
To be able to call
Each friend's life giver
My mother!

by Sarvesh Shyam

23

Finding My Angel

Born to a loving family, bought up in a prosperous state,
A masters' degree and a good job, was all in my fate.
Then he came and brought a blossoming spring in life,
Madly in love with each other, we became husband-wife.
Everything was perfect, so planned to move further,
I put everything aside and prepared to be a mother.
We did loads of planning, pending holidays were done,
Finances check, car check, and also house redone.
Then started the journey, we thought will be light,
Never in our dreams, we thought it will become our biggest fight.
Few months of self-assessment, and many a medical test,
Also bowed our head to deities, and whatever people suggest.
Then happened the serious talk, with IVF plans on my card,
WHY ME? – never hit me when - I saw others in the ward.
Their stories were heart numbing, tough times they went through,
But all has a dream in eyes, it raised the strength to pursue.
I gathered my own strength, love of family made me stand,
IVF was finally done, 21 days wait, and then got scanned.
The longing of so many days just took a sudden turn,
It Strangled my love and fun – the result I got to learn.
Feeling of motherhood was great as 21 days elapsed,
But that evening, I can't tell how my world collapsed.

Morning of 22nd day, I decided to make my 1st day,
A day to start another hope, without any dismay.
Something happened inside me, I remember it was 5th of May.
I skipped a beat seeing that little pea in the scan, I can now confess,
Our little princess, with angel eyes, came to us on x-mas.
Could not take my eyes off her, can never forget that sight,
Life is again beautiful with our sunshine, our little delight.

by Neha Prashar Verma

24

Middle Age

This is where I want to stand,
Underneath a shower of yellow leaves and sunshine,
Filtered between dried branches of lattice,
That criss-cross shadows upon my face.
Not so young and not so green behind my ears,
...Or anywhere else for that matter.
I'm glad I still have sunshine before the brown and black.
I'm glad for flowers and fruit before the brown and black.
And seed that I leave behind,
That are still green behind the ears.

by Padma

25

The Valiant Chef

by Aryaman Chakraborty

There was a pleasant ambience at Café Luigi's, the place was bustling with customers. This Sunday was a particularly crowded one as it was the start of holidays in America. Maria, the head chef was overworked with the crowd. She had been working since 5 in the morning and had gone 7 hours without a break, even though she desperately needed one. Luckily, she was saved by her partner John Monroe who arrived for his evening shift a bit early.

Relieved to see him, she immediately took off her apron, hung it on the counter, washed her face, and went out for a smoke. Taking the cigarette out, she lit it using her lighter and took a small puff. All the stress she had was washed away as she sat back on the stool outside and leaned back against her wall and closed her eyes to take a power nap. At that moment one of the waiters barged outside interrupting her break. This made her very angry, and she shouted

"WHAT IS IT? WHY CAN'T YOU LET ME REST FOR A SECOND?"

The waiter got scared by her sudden burst of anger and in a trembling voice, he said "I am very sorry ma'am, but we have run out of a couple of vegetables and are understaffed right now. The chef said that since you were on a break you could go and get it."

Maria sighed, when will I get a break, she thought. Taking the list from the waiter's hand, she picked up her handbag, went to the changing room, and changed out of her chef's uniform. She exited the restaurant and made her way to the grocery store down the street. It took her 10 mins to reach the store and as she walked in, two shady guys wearing black caps and black hoodies walked out. Their clothes raised her suspicion, but she dismissed them from her mind. After she entered the store, she went around in search of the ingredients in her list. It was at that time that she noticed the quantity was not specified in the list. She hunted for her phone in the bag, but it was not there. At first, she thought she dropped it, so she spent 15 minutes searching the stores and frantically checking her pockets. It was later that she realized that she must have left it in the restaurant. She sighed again, she had to walk back to ask about the quantity and to take her phone from the restaurant. As she made her way to the back door of the restaurant, she felt something was wrong. The restaurant was unusually silent, and the crowd could not have died down within such a short time.

Nevertheless, she did not think much about it and went into the restroom through the back door and directly into her changing room to look for her phone. It was a moment she heard the voice of a man whispering

"Go lock the back door and make sure no one comes in or escapes"

A few seconds later she heard the sound of the latch on the door and the sound of the zip tie to enforce the lock and make sure no one can come in. Maria's heart started beating very fast, she was in the middle of a hostage situation and the hostage-takers did not know she was there. She wanted to move from the room and run away but her body was not obeying her. She was frozen in fear and had no chance of escaping. She also had no idea if the hostages were dead or alive. The moment her thoughts diverted to the hostages, she suddenly thought of her friends and co-workers and how they expected her to notice the situation and call the police. Call! She remembered that her phone was locked with her and she could try to call the police. She reached for her phone in the bag and that moment she realized that she had dropped it somewhere. Due to the fear, she forgot that she had dropped her phone. Her panic increased, she was trapped with no escape and if she was discovered, her life would be in danger. The only good thing she noticed that the hostage-takers hadn't noticed her yet.

This also meant they weren't looking for her. Looking outside through the gap underneath her door, she checked to see if the coast is clear. She heard nothing and carefully opened the door slightly. The restaurant was completely silent she did not see anyone in sight. she came out and closed the door behind her and made her way to the back door. When she reached the door, she saw that it was locked with a zip-tie, she did not have a knife with her or else she could have cut through it. It was at that moment a daring thought kicked in, she could go slowly to the kitchen and get a knife. She wanted to run away but her survival instinct kicked in and she had to find a way out here alive. The bathroom window was too small for anyone to get out so that could not be used. She using the tables as cover slowly made her way to the kitchen. Just as she reached the table nearest to the kitchen, one of the guys came from the storage room, carrying a machine gun. Reflexively she went under the table and hid with the help of the long table cloth. The man was very powerful, judging by his build, wearing a ski mask and had a tattoo going down his neck. He did a quick survey to check if anyone was around and then went back. When Maria heaved a sigh of relief she realized, she was so much in fear that she held her breath while he was in the room. Finally, she made her way to the counter and pepped inside the kitchen through the door. All the hostages were tied up and gagged and one had been shot in the leg. She wanted to go in and free the hostages but that would get her caught and also extinguish their last hope of being rescued.

She took one of the steak knives from the counter and start making her way back the same way she came in. Luckily without incident, she was able to reach the back door and started cutting through the zip-tie with her steak knife. She was so focused on cutting that she paid no attention to her surroundings. The moment she finished cutting through the zip-tie and opened the door, one of the men saw her and pointed their gun towards her. Seeing her way out so close, she decided to make a break for it and just ran out the man shot after her missing almost all his shots. One of his shots hit her on the shoulders. So much adrenaline was rushing through her body that she did not notice the fact that she had been shot and ran as far as she could. The thug wanted to run after her, but the other one stopped him and said, "She won't last with such a wound, she will die and by the time the cops get here, we will be long gone."

Maria ran as far as her legs could take her. She was strong but kept feeling very tired and wanted to lie down. However, her heart kept telling her to run, to reach the police so that she could save many lives and not regret it. She was barely conscious as she reached the precinct, a uniformed officer held her as she was going to fall. With all her remaining strength she uttered "Ca....Cafe L...Luigi" and then fell unconscious.

Maria woke up with excruciating pain on her shoulders and the feel of an IV being injected into her arm. It took her a moment to realize that she was in a hospital. She sprang up from her bed suddenly, remembering about the hostage situation. The nurse who came to treat her got startled and almost dropped the tray which she was carrying. She kept the tray beside and calmed Maria.

"It's ok. You are safe."

"What happened at Café Luigi's? Was I too late?" she said in a trembling voice. She was frightened at the very thought of leaving her friends and now thought that she should have been with them.

The nurse replied "They caught the hostage-takers just as they were escaping. You saved the day."

"What were they after? Why were my friends taken, hostage?"

"They were after diamonds worth of five million dollars that the owner had kept in the restaurant safe. This was the diamonds he had won as the best restaurant in the whole of DC. However, they failed because you reached the cops on time. A detective is here to take your statement and then you can rest."

Maria was happy, she heaved a sigh of relief and laid back on the bed. This was the most interesting and hellish day of her life. However, it was finally over.

26

Burning Hands Behind My Spicy Fries

by Minnu Ranjith

I looked through the window when I got a message from Amma(mom) “meet me before you leave”. She is sitting under the maple tree and painting a picture. This is her nostalgic corner, the place where she escapes when she feels haunted by her hometown memories. The wheelchair waited nearby asking her “when are you coming back to my lap, honey?” Yeah, this is gifted by the road accident she met with when I was just 4yrs old. Her spine was damaged as a result of the incident, and the doctors asked her not to travel long distances, or rest in the same postures for too long as it may hinder the blood flow and make the condition worse. She uses a wheelchair to move around, even though she can walk or stand without it for short periods. She is a strong woman and never surrendered to her destiny. She is the senior graphic designer of a big brand and earns a huge amount. She loves to feed me with the authentic dishes of her native place. I love ”idiyappam” drenched in sweet thick coconut milk along with egg roast, vegetable stew, and crispy dosas with spicy coconut chutney and sambar. Even though she can’t prepare it as quickly as she used to before the accident, she makes sure to treat me with some wonderful dishes whenever she can.

"Oh! I am getting late for my flight". I packed some dresses and arranged my official files for the international presentation and treaded towards Amma to say goodbye. She was drawing a picture of a girl, her eyes were full of life, and smile with innocence. "Who is this ?" I asked, "Karthu" the answer came quickly with a sigh. She handed me a gift and said give this to her.

I was thinking of Karthu throughout my flight until sleep took over me. When I landed in Amma's hometown, rain welcomed me saying they are missing their Neelambari (my mom). She never came back after dad took her to "Florida" soon after their marriage. But she always tells stories about her land, "God's own country". My company staff welcomed me and took me to my hotel in the "Periyar" river valley. The cool wind gushed to my face flooding my mind with thoughts of Karthu, the main character in Amma's stories.

The conference and presentations went well, and the management seemed to be happy with my work. Ammamma (grandma) called me and said, "I will send Achuthan to pick you up". Achuthan mama (uncle) came when the meeting was over.

When I was about to reach Amma's ancestral home, I felt as though I was living the many stories Amma had filled my mind with. The narrow roads through the coconut groves ended before a green paddy field. "Car won't go to the house you need to walk a bit, better to take off your heels, it is a muddy lane," Achuthan mama said. I removed my heels and touched Amma's motherland barefoot, I got goosebumps, my eyes flooded with tears.

I took a deep breath saying, "I have come to see you for my mother, who misses you dearly". I could see the "Naalukettu"(the old traditional home of Kerala) and

Ammamma eagerly waiting for me. Kelappan chettan was walking behind me carrying my luggage. Ammamma had a nilavilakku (lighted lamp) in her hand(the traditional welcome), Nangeli poured water from "Kindi" to wash my feet before I entered the house. "Come-on in" Ammamma, took me inside.

It was a huge house and there was no visible fence but luscious paddy fields, coconut groves, and streams surrounded us and stretched out in all directions taking turns to hide the horizon from me. I got a tender coconut as a welcome drink. Keeping a set of "mundum neriyathum" (dress) near me she asked to take a dip in the pond.

On my way to the pond, my eyes got stuck on the staircase, where Amma and Karthu used to spend their lazy afternoons gossiping. Karthu used to give a special Penknife head massage. That is the act of supposedly killing the lice from the head. It is done by smoothy pressing the blunt knife tip on the head with a shh.. shh.. sound, and it is so soothing that Amma wanted her to do the same even when there are no lice left, by the end of massages, she used to fell asleep due to the relaxation it brings in. The pond was so huge, and it had steps and some hideouts to change clothes. Amma and Karthu used to jump into the pond and see who could jump in from the furthest step. The next game was by staying underwater holding their breath, the one who stays longer duration will win. I too tried this while taking bath with the herbal powder Nangeli brought for me. Amma is the one who taught Karthu swimming, they used to swim criss-cross in this pond. I sat on the steps immersed in the bliss of this ambiance, a little fish started playing with my fingertips immersed in the water which tickled me.

I had tea with "ilayada", "Pazham pori", "unniyappam", "kozhukatta" and so many snacks all homemade. No wonder Amma's stories have always had a flavour of good food, everything was new and yummy, some of them Amma made for me but it tasted different here. Ammamma kept on asking about Amma, she seems to miss her daughter and sighed thinking of her bad fate. Nangeli was peeping from the kitchen to hear what we were sharing. She was tying Jasmin and Kanakambarm to decorate on my hair. "At 6 O'clock we can go to Krishna's temple, before that you can light the lamp in Sarpa Kavu (Abode of Snakes, is a traditional natural sacred space seen near traditional homes in Kerala state of South India) and Kallara (grave where great grandfather was buried)". Ammamma was relived see that I had lit the lamp in Sarpa kavu, because as perJyothsyan" (astrologer) I and Amma had "sarppadosham", so they had performed some Pooja (rituals) for that. She applied some turmeric paste on my forehead. Ammamma found joy in s introducing me to the people around saying "nte Neelunte kuttiya", she's my Neelu's daughter. After darshan at the temple she bought me some red, blue, and black glass bangles from Gopalan chettan's shop... it was for sure she saw her daughter in me and enjoyed doing things for me.

I slept in Amma's room, Nangeli kept "jeerakavellam" in a jug. The room was full of Amma's belongings, her paintings, books, old trunk with her dresses, bangles, karimanimala, silver anklets. I packed some of them to give to her. There was an old photograph of Amma and Karthu. It evoked tales of her.

It was during the floods in 1967, many people lost their family and belongings. Ammamma was supplying the basics to the flood victims in her "Kettuvallam" (houseboat) and then someone said "Pushkaran brought a maid", she nodded okay and continued her work. But her mind was too preoccupied with the destruction that she didn't pay any attention to him. While debarking Grandma was shocked to see this 12-year-old girl Karthu in sheer "Thorthmundu" (towel) and gave her "Melmundu" to cover her bare chest. Amma was happy to see Karthu almost her age. She was a lean dark innocent girl. Although she was initially sad, they became fast friends.

This is how Amma portrayed her, "What should I say about her, she was a girl without illusions. she never saw her beauty, the strive towards selflessness. Without her unique ways my childhood will not be this incredulously magnificent, you may call her a maid, but she is much more than that. Her presence always gave me a calm assurance of faithfully loving you. Her cooking skills were excellent. Everyone loved the spicy fish fry she prepared, by grounding bird-eyed chilies, shallots, and rock-salt on the stone grinder. Then marinate the fish with that paste, wrap it in banana leaf and bake it with firewood. This dish is her masterpiece but made her hands burning out of the heat from the chilies. I used to apply coconut oil to calm that down. we have a special invisible bond. After some years Karthu became pregnant with a young herding boy. When he heard the news, he fled. Ammamma built a small house for them. Now her son has a job, and he takes care of her".

While having my sumptuous lunch, with "Thalum thakarem", "Parippum murigelem", "Payattila thoran", "Matthapoo curry", "Chuttaracha chammanthi" … the dishes you can never buy with Zomato or Uber eats... you may get some of those leaf powders on amazon under the label of Superfoods. Ammamma smiled and said, "this is a special dish Karthu bought for you when she heard you are visiting today". I opened that banana leaf-wrapped "chala pollichatu" is tasted great and satisfied my taste buds. I badly wanted to meet her...

After lunch, I walked through the narrow lane in the backyard. The lane ended in-front of a beautiful small house where Karthu was waiting for me. She came running with an innocent smile filled with joy and called me "Kochambratye .... you look just like your mom". We walked towards the "PadinjaraValappu" where they used to enjoy the sunset, sat there, and chatted for a long duration.

She pointed towards a spot on the other side of the river, "that is where I was born, and the flood took away everything, my family, my home" she sighed. "That's when "Pushkaran Chettan" brought me to your grandmother," she said.

The orange sun rays made Karthu more graceful... you cannot relate anything of her to the beauty standards, but once she smiles all that innocence and the earthiness made her the most beautiful woman.

It was time for my flight. I clicked some photos with her and gifted them the gold bangle which Amma send for her. She couldn't believe her eyes... that was the first piece of gold in her life. While I reluctantly waved goodbye.... tears started rolling through her cheeks. I don't have any words for how I felt while coming back... Some relationships are priceless, words fail to do any justice in explaining them. I have never seen such unadulterated people, people without masks are rare to find nowadays.

Many women in our world sacrifice their lives for others and fade away by making others happy and comfortable. They may not have done anything special to gain recognition. But they are the real gems who make this world bright and beautiful.

UP

IN

ARMS

27

Unholy

Thighs bleeding
With the so-called impurity
Every time I'm shunned
Out of my own kitchen
To not stench up
The holy place of God,
Hanging my head in shame
With every drop of blood,
On the maroon bedsheet,
That cannot go in the machine,
Hiding the polythene bag
With my dirty identity,
Behind my back, from dad
Behind the leaflets of newspaper,
The same man, who cried out in joy
With the birth of his baby girl!

Tears flowing from unbearable pain
Only to be told by motherly women
That I'm a child bearing machine,
No privilege to complain,
So I weep silent tears
In one gloomy corner of my room
Curtains drawn in, to hide
My tear jerked face from the world!

I’m called filthy
For every underwear with a stain
I'm 22 years old and
I cannot scream out from pain
I call out my Lord’s name
Only to be met with a strike
Cause I’m an unholy whore
A freak, the Lord wouldn’t like,
Now, whom do I turn to,
To end this ache,
My God won’t listen to me
Cause I’m a bleeding mistake,
I know this’ll all end one day
When I’m six feet under
And out of the society’s way!

by Namrada Varshini

28

Dear Sister

Dear Sister, we are the same, you and I
The same worries, anxieties, and insecurities deep within us thrive
We wonder at the same nuances, comparisons, and expectations of ourselves we want to meet,
Both externally and from within, we ask ourselves the same question, 'How will I be perceived?'

Why do we choose to judge and misrepresent, sometimes hold each other down?
Make this world harder and tougher in an endless pattern which is already abound?
Would it be so hard to hold your hand and uplift you, wipe the tears away?
Tell you you're beautiful, that I feel your struggle and I'm with you all of the way?

Spread lessons of positivity regardless of whether you're a friend, stranger, or family,
But the moment passes, with words left unsaid, and silence leaves a whisper of things we could not be
Let's break this barrier of communication between you and me
What separates us is not real; it's a figment of our imagination of some unknown decree

Aren't the patterns in the sky we see the same, doesn't the wind on our cheek makes us smile subliminally
Just as is the grass we frolic in, and feel against a rain fell day is the same– both calm and dewy?
We share the same feelings of loneliness, doubt, and oppression
Let the self-created walls around no longer help us stay blissfully ignorant
If we could all but join hands and break free
Of whatever imaginary chains we think we see

Let us love each other, the way we are meant to be
I don't want to hold you down, as you're my brethren, my sanctity.
Dear Sister, we are the same, you and I,
Sisters of the heart and soul, even if we live under some other veil or disguise

by Samyuktha Ramachandran

29

Defeated… Never Again

Her tiny little form, half in disarray
Her innocent mind, too small to discern
Cringing...as her back meets the wall
Totally Frozen...unable to bellow!

Slowly as it dawned, oh so evil
The rage inside, grew with her
No right had he, to grope and probe
Her self-esteem, was not to rob.

Yet too fragile, as that she was
She held her horses, for the tide.
The passage of time, saw her rise
In grit and might, just as her stride.

She stormed in war, that she waged
Cast bleeding wounds, as she ravaged
To the kill, destroying mercilessly
She revolted, slashing fearlessly.

The Truth sparkling , did emerge
From the edges of a murky past
Defeated, she will never again be
Her body...her rules... to the last!!!

by Nalini Vipin

30

Change

I was brought up to believe in a maternal society
One meant to outline the strength of a woman in all her glory
To be respected and treated with both grace and dignity
Our society and its beliefs have fallen into a well of shame; it's a sorrowful pity

India from her glory days, has entered into a dystopian phase
Regarding rape, a term not given importance due, that which everyone thinks and never says
A cultural change of mentality is required to awaken all from the daze
Of tolerance towards perpetrated crime, and patriarchy bastardised in these inhuman ways

After the bestiality of the Nirbhaya case, we thought change is in the air
Such injustice deserved consequences dire
The indictment of the four, though took time, seemed something akin to fair
Hatred, misogyny, and sadism must stop, a common goal we seemed to share

8 year later, what do we have to show?
Episodes of cruelty repeated in Hathras, Kathaua,
Hyderabad, and Unnao
Of Children and innocents, such detestation
and horror cannot go
Unpunished; The seeds of justice must be sowed

This is not how our society was raised to see, how malignant
the acts of some people could really be
They were Innocent, wide eyed, to be cherished with their
own goals and dreams
One reported case in India every 18 minutes, it seems
One of worst crime against women with a poor conviction
rate emphasizes justice's mediocrity

I knew a girl, independent strong and free, who found
herself in a situation of similarity
Of a man who thought he would take what he felt he was
owed, and she would succumb dutifully
The circumstances and perhaps pure luck led to the crime
not committed in its entirety
However, trauma, fear, loss, and heartache that followed
were a reality.

One lucky girl in one thousand, but yet many more with a
strong sense to survive
'My experiences will not define me, I will fight every day
that I am alive,
To protect my integrity, and fight for justice for a cause is a
goal I must contrive'

Let us fight today, and then fight every day, for the safety of women till that day arrives.

by Samyuktha Ramachandran

31

To My Dear Satanist

Doubt not,
the depth of my devotion,
My sacrificial heart remains,
as certain and restless as the rain,

Thus,
When I leave you,
It will be owed to:
The icy downpours,
of your summoned snowstorms,
Ceaselessly bruising,
my flames into losing,
Until they're repulsed,
by your cavalier cult.

(written with the emotionally abused woman in mind)

by Christina Triplett-Wagenknecht

32

Raven Flames

Skies covered in monochromatic stars,
Winds from your glacial love, burn in bright black,
White rainbows reflect light, from vibrant hearts,

Gallons of gasoline can't save what's ours,
Where fire is forbidden, and hijacked,
Skies covered in monochromatic stars,

Passion mirrored by your phlegmatic Mars,
Unconditional on counterattack,
White rainbows reflect light, from vibrant hearts,

Lively nights put behind the pale bars,
Of your arctic, prosaic zodiac,
Skies covered in monochromatic stars,

My golden loyalty dissolved, now sparse,
Into a dismissed abyss, stomped and smacked,
White rainbows reflect light, from vibrant hearts,

Spectrums of sincere treasures torched to scars,
By a decade of raven flames you've cracked,
Skies covered in monochromatic stars,
White rainbows reflect light, from vibrant hearts.

(a villanelle written with the emotionally abused woman in mind)

by Christina Triplett-Wagenknecht

33

Mother

Is the dawn of time
just a metaphor
for the birth
of a woman?

For
how would we know
when time began?
All we know

is mankind's existence
because a woman
chose
to bring pain
upon herself
so that a baby's cry
would herald
the continuation
of humanity.

Pain is rarely
called noble.
I know though
that giving birth
is redemption for

every sin, every mistake
I've ever committed.

And so,
keep bringing me
that noblest of pain.
I will die
over and over
just so that I may learn
the sacrifice of a
mother's love.
Let me live
a thousand births
so that I may see
the single smile
on her face
when I grab her finger,
like the sunflower
meets the sun.

As my inhale becomes her exhale,
perhaps
I may finally know
the searing ache and
unconditional love
of
a mother's heart.

by Divya Om Manoharan

34

Life! Let's Fight!

I got drenched in the rain today
And my makeup caked
My tear stains are showing
And my mask got torn
My armour's showing a chink
And am feeling weak and tired too
I know am strong but am exhausted today.
But Life, if you think you have got me
Let just tomorrow come.
I will sleep off early today
And I will have my little cry
I will hug my baby to sleep
And tomorrow I will be all fine.
I will look you in the eye
And fight you blow for blow
And when you stop to take some rest
I will say, "Let's fight some more."

by Baishakhi Mukherjee

35

Girls, We Need To Take A Stand

Dear Girls,

We can fight for ourself,

If you are slim or fatty,
Dark or whatever ,
You just don't give a fuck,
You are here for yourself not for others.

Dear girls,
It's ok if they don't choose you,
let them go,
Don't beg for love,
Just remember you are your own,

Dear girls,
A man don't complete you,
You complete yourself,
Love yourself.

by Riya Om

36

Enjoy Being You

by Sujitha Ryali

Life in a village surrounded by greenery is just heaven. The fresh air always touches and greets me when I open my window.

The rustle invited me to step out to play. The clouds came down & it started drizzling and then steadily. I raised my head pointing my face towards the sky.

My clothes became wet, and I pulled a kid out of me dancing. This is usually me, cheerful always. But... A day in my life… & it turned out to be a story to read.

***

A short story of a girl who realized, it's always inner beauty that shines & has learned to maintain a smile while making her surroundings happy regardless of her mood swings.

Until days ago, the happy girl would spread a smile all her way greeting people every day.

Even in the materialistic age of today, she led a simple yet beautiful life being good at heart spreading positivity. With an interest to always do something for the people, she started

Herbalism years ago for providing inexpensive medicine availability for her village.

During the day while she works on the research on herbs, evenings she dedicates her couple of hours to journaling exploring different places in the village & spends time there with people to understand unhygienic conditions.

While having a tremendous and meaningful life living closely with people, she was nevertheless unhappy about her appearance. Even though she was fond of fashion ever since she was young looking at others, she never took it so seriously.

But one day while on her way to the lake to spend a beautiful evening with kids as part of journaling, she saw a crowd gathered at the place.

She went closer to see what had happened and her excitement had no bounds seeing a couple of girls. Their special attires caught her eyes.

She was very impressed with the way people are dressed there and the way they were getting treated by everyone who saw their fashion. The moment she saw villagers abuzz with excitement about the girls, she desired to experience that.

So, she thought, changing the clothing style would bring her special love and attention which she felt missing living as a simple girl.

Hence, to present herself better in the world, she tried different outfits but unfortunately didn't succeed in carrying fashion either people's attention.

She is mentally deteriorating day by day thinking she is not a beautiful woman and started berating herself. The smile on her face disappeared automatically from the moment she started comparing herself to others.

She was even reluctant to talk to people like before, pulling herself down that she was not pretty at fashion.

A few days later, when she opened the door in the morning, a plant with a note appeared in front.

It was written,

"People might be better at fashion - people might be better at appearance - people might be better at everything but you are best being you. We are missing your smile and fun.

Regards, without a name."

The tears in her eyes rolled down reading that. She took a deep breath and realized how she was and how she became looking back on her days.

The moment she realized she was not "she", the moment she stopped comparing herself with people, the sadness in her heart disappeared. Her jaws expanded with her smile back after many days.

Eventually, she regained the joy in her heart and began to like her regardless of what she was wearing & how she is.

Even though the plant is placed by her with a note, her grief suddenly disappeared.

The day she noticed people's attention when she was appearing dull, the day she realized her surroundings were not joyful as before; she was no longer comfortable looking at her negative emotions.

To make her come out from chasing to be a reflection of someone, she decided to do something to bring her happiness back. Hence, she placed the plant by herself consoling her.

The unspoken words by villagers through eye contact conveyed, it's not what you wear & how you look. Instead, what you are & how you are is all matters.

Thereafter, she started loving everything about herself & appeared to be a happy girl always rather suffering from self-criticism on her appearance.

***

And thus, she became a girl who never missed to smile and always try to make her surroundings happy even when she was sad.

Please remember - The fashion may appear attractive - but it's always inner beauty that shines & the personality that captures the heart.

Always be grateful for what you are & never chase to be a reflection of someone. Enjoy being you. Never let your inner beauty fade away.

HEAVY
HEART

37

Pastel Praise

Her head bows as she goes,
So she can walk around the bugs-
though they'd bite,
And sandcastles-
though they'd break,
Thereby, she misses the blossoming bushes-
Praise in pastel shades,
passing by her side.

by Christina Triplett-Wagenknecht

38

Where You Belong

I was always told to be myself
But which part of me do I belong to?
numerous voices and opinions
have shaped my beliefs,
moulded this mind
that once lacked ideology
maybe they had to tame the woman in me,
comfortably unaware of the mechanisms
that prepare you to face the world,
We are merely reflections of their advices
their lives and circumstances chained with ours,
Some say it is essential character building,
I might regurgitate
because I don't know any better,
I failed to associate with the numerous versions
stacked inside me,
But I was also told to listen to my inner voice,
discarding multiple identities that reside within me,
split personality not just a rare enigma behind bolted doors,
we are milder representations of
the extremities that shape disorders,
Somewhere underneath many layers of norm ridden grime,
there is an echo you are familiar with,
inherent wisdom your cells breathe,
intuitive tunes that compose resonating melodies,

I hope you don’t have to dig up your soul for too long,
to find your precious song..

by Nitya Bhatia

39

Imminent

I feel like a black hole.
Swallowing every pain,
Every hurt,
Every thought,
Every scream,
Into a gravitational void.
And if they rise,
I swallow
More times than once.
An invisible hand inside my throat,
Pushing things back to the black.
To the safety of the void,
Where no one can see nor sense,
The heavy pretence.
The weight builds up.
The space breaks down.
Is it destruction or resurrection
This imminent Big Bang?

by Padma

40

Mother's Love

A blank paper could answer well if asked,
how would be a mom's love look like.
But in my wildest thoughts I ever wondered
how would it look like.
Imaginations took me for a ride into nature;
my all-time favourite place.
Is it something like how the clouds melt
themselves into raindrops?
There I met a definition where theories and
rules of life exists no more.
Triumphed with joy I ran back to my study
to pen down that overwhelming emotion.
I went on filling up the paper but the letters
seem to be invisible.
And finally the definition was ready resulting
a perfect blank paper.

by Maria Mappilassery

41

The Whisperers

Do you hear the whisperers?

The hushed speakers of dark realities,
The camouflaged voices of deep cavities,
The mischievous lurkers of quiet insecurities?

If you hear them, listen...

Listen to their doubts of crazy primitivity,
Listen to their laughs of wicked reciprocity,
Listen to their tales of casual frivolity.

Then talk...

Talk to them versions of people you once knew,
Talk to them and tell them you value their views,
Talk to them and comfort them for they're all in you.

by Ambika Rao

42

Fleeting And Beautiful

An airy mist,
Dewdrops on the grass,
The colours on a dragon fly's wings.
Beautiful and fleeting
They come and go,
Like your memories.
I reach out to touch
And I touch the nothingness.
And yet
And yet right before the nothingness
I find everything, I find you.
Fleeting and beautiful

by Baishakhi Mukherjee

43

Epiphany

I've lost myself,
Bit by cellular bit.
Every step forward,
On this journey of life
I forgot to take her with me.
Not consciously
Categorically though.
For everyone I accommodated,
She made space.
By getting off.
By getting left behind.
And I didn't notice
Didn't realise
Until one day,
I came across a piece of me
A memory
And it hits me with such grief,
This death that I have just realised,
Many, many rebirths after.

by Padma

44

Hold Me Close

Hold me close
in a way that will
make me forget
that there ever was a day
when your hug
wasn't a part
of me.

Fill me up
with your love so immense
that I can scarcely
believe
the pitiful excuse
for a life
I lived before.

I know you.
I have seen you.
Weren't you the one
who told me that
my mother would
take your place

If I came down to Earth?
Here I am.

Why didn't you tell me
though
that she is but
an atom of your
whole?

Why didn't you tell me
that
she is made of
the same essence?

I learnt it my way.
And it took too long -
three decades.

Don't make me wait now.
Reveal yourself
so that
I don't spend another
three decades
learning about how
the face of God
is the face of... Her.

That my introduction to
the Divine Feminine
was always
supposed

to
be
my
Mother.

by Divya Om Manoharan

45

My Walls

Walls are placed for protection from others taking pieces of me away.
High places are where I go, no one can find or seek me for I only know.
There are times I feel I am drowning in this pool of suffocating water.
I do not ask for any intervention, I am who I am
I am a bringer of light for I see my own glow.
I shall surface in due time with the need to flow.

by Maria Wynnyckyj

46

Broken Mirror

The satisfying shattering of smashed glass
Only the handle remains of the cracked cup.
The shards like shrapnel fly back,
Embedding themselves into my skin.
"If you hurt me, I'll hurt you back", says the mirror.
The pain is welcome.
Maybe this bloodletting will purge me.
But will it diminish the despair?
I feel the pressure build up in my head,
In my chest
Heading towards explosion
Emotions smeared across the silvered surface
The mirror just cracks a smile.

by Padma

47

Womanhood

My womanhood weighs me down
like I'm iron chained and flung into the ocean,
there are days when
the sorry from my tongue
has lost all its connotations to begin!
Why do you call a woman, an angel
and define her to be a honeyed glacé
well, I want to be Michael
plunging Lucifer in his cage!
My womanhood destroys me
where I shove my ghosted heart
with pieces of red stained glass
in hopes I'd bleed out my womanhood
into your chauvinistic whiskey glass!
I'm not your bride in a gossamer veil
I hold bronze daggers, each telling a tale,
I'm not Luna thriving on borrowed light,
I'm Dawn, letting you bask in my holy might!
I don't loathe my womanhood, it's just rage
that I'm smothered and trampled on
in this hell-bent hegemonizing age!
I'm a warrior, my scars
and womanhood, should be my pride
instead they break my mind,
under long sleeves and a tan,

they want me to hide!
What is freedom when,
I'm at a war with myself
and my bleeding thighs
but I sure will not be annihilated
this bigoted society can try!

by Namrada Varshini

48

Best Friends

by Soham Maliye

Aastha heard her mom complaining to her dad. "She rejects all the photos I send her way. How will she get married if she keeps finding faults with every guy she sees!?"

Her dad was silent. As usual. Mom continued louder than before "She isn't getting any younger you see!!" to which her dad replied "Girls these days have different ideologies. She will eventually get married. Just let her be." Ah! Dad! Her saviour!

She heard loud noises from the kitchen followed by her mother's angry voice shouting "I will wait for the day you father-daughter duo realize your mistake. Hope it won't be too late by then."

This was an everyday scenario at Aastha's house these days. How she wished to move to a PG like her other friends and stay as far away from family as possible.

She took out her phone to distract herself from this never-ending drama. And she found the perfect distraction. A message from her newly married best friend Hita from London. "Hey, bestie! Wassup?" it read.

She wrote back "You know the normal 'get married' stuff. I'm so done with this torture!"

Quick came the response, "Dude! Don't give in to pressure. Take your time and get married only when you feel you are ready."

How lucky was Hita to have found her Mr. Perfect quite early and fly to London, away from all these emotional blackmails to begin her new chapter of life, she thought.

***

Hita, who usually took ages to get out of bed, was up in an instant. She rushed to the kitchen to fix breakfast for her husband before he left for the office. She couldn't believe she was in the kitchen at 6 in the morning! It was still dark outside and cold.

She looked around at the empty house and went to the window to find the streets empty as well. There was pin-drop silence everywhere. She missed the ever-buzzing streets and the incessant honks in traffic. Wasn't she the one who hated vehicle sounds back home and the one who shouted at the guys riding motorcycles to get a silencer for their bikes!?

She opened her phone to find Aastha's message. "Yeah. Thanks, bro! Wish you were here. Miss you. Good morning"

Aastha had dozed off again the previous evening while chatting with her and she had responded first thing in the morning.

"Miss you too," she wrote back.

"Oye. Having your favourite biryani prepared by mom. Wanna have some?" She saw a picture of her favourited dish. She craved for it.

How lucky was Aastha to have her mom so close to pamper and cook for her every day. Hope she doesn't get married soon and enjoy that life for a little longer, Hita thought.

***

A year passed by. Aastha finally gave in to her mother's wishes or in her words, 'demand' and got married.

Her life was much busier than usual. She had to change 3 modes of transportation to reach the office. She would be dead tired by the time she reached home. She hardly had time for anything else now. She couldn't even respond to Hita's messages or calls.

***

Hita was tired of this loneliness. She needed her friends more than ever. Alas! They were all busy with their lives. Even Aastha was busy these days. She eventually stopped texting/calling her not having heard back from her several times. Though she had made some new friends, she couldn't connect with anyone like she did with the people back home. She was learning to enjoy her own company.

***

Eventually, both the friends lost touch and their interactions were limited to likes and comments on each other's posts on social media.

One day during a lunch break while scrolling through her phone, Aastha found Hita's posts of yummy snacks she had prepared every day of the week. Those dishes looked inviting. She looked at the half-burnt dosa in her box she had prepared in a rush. Wish she had the time to prepare such delicacies. For the first time in her life, she felt envious of Hita and her life.

She asked herself if this mechanical life was worth it. She had always longed for a simple life. When her husband told her about a job opening in IBM, she wanted to say 'no' when he said, "With the EMI on our new car and my mother's medical expenses, a hike in salary would be beneficial". She had no choice but to say yes.

Just then she received a call from her mother.

"How are you?"

"I'm a good mom. Hope you and dad are good too."

"Yeah. Yeah, we are good. Any good news yet?"

"Mom, please. You know I don't want to have kids so soon."

"You girls these days don't understand anything. Listen to me. You shouldn't delay such things…." her mom went on.

She said there was a meeting in 5 minutes and cut the call.

She blamed herself for thinking all this nagging would be over if she got married. All she wanted was to go back home and hit the bed which was a luxury these days.

What was she doing with life? Why and how did she lose interest in life? Does she have a purpose anymore?

***

Hita checked her phone first thing in the morning to find a series of rejection emails from the companies she had applied for a job.

Among the pile, she found an email which read 'Congratulate Aastha on her new job at IBM'. For the first time in her life, Hita felt a twinge of envy. She could have been Aastha's colleague if she was in India. She would have had a purpose in life! Moreover, she always wanted to be an independent woman. Finding a job in a foreign country is on a temporary visa was so hard!

She had no reason to get out of bed. What was she doing with life apart from cooking food 3 times a day?

Just then her phone buzzed. A message from her cousin. She was relieved to find something to distract her.

"Hey! Wassup? It's been ages" it read.

She replied "Hey yes! How have you been?"

"Good. So, are you working now?"

"No. Not yet."

She was about to type, "I'm looking for a job but it's so difficult to find one here…" came the response, "Hahaha. So, you are a housewife now."

She wanted to call him up and give an earful. Instead, she replied "LOL" and switched off her phone.

Was she a housewife now? Will she ever be able to work? Is she losing her self-confidence day by day? Will she ever be happy in life?

***

Aastha received a message from Hita. "Hey, gal. How are you? Hope you are free."

"Yes, I am. Tell me. How are you?" Hita wrote back.

"I am good Hita. Listen. I'm coming to India next month during Christmas break. Let's catch up if you are free."

Aastha was excited "Oh my. Yes. I can make the time any day. Let me know your dates."

***

Hita was nervous. What if Aastha talks about her life at IBM a lot and how much she enjoys working there. Will I be able to hide my feelings? Can I pretend to be enjoying my life? I should fake it she thought.

Aastha had a second thought. Shall I call her up and say there's an emergency and I can't make it? Will she talk about her colourful and peaceful life in London? And about her trips to Europe? She looked at her reflection in the mirror and tried to smile. Looks fake, work on it she said to herself and got into a cab.

***

One long look at each other and the initial doubts vanished into thin air. The two best friends talked for hours. They poured their hearts out and talked about how one was jealous of the other's life.

It was the best day they had in a long time. They both promised to stay in touch and make time for each other.

They bid goodbye and went back to their respective homes with the most natural broadest smiles. They realized that "the grass is always greener on the other side". They understood that one cannot have everything in life, and they need to learn to embrace life and live happily with whatever lifestyle they are blessed with while striving hard for a better one rather than getting depressed and comparing their life with others.

Life wasn't easy but it was better!

49

The Garden Snake

by Maxine Mathew

It felt weird being back in my childhood room after nearly a decade. The air in the room still lay heavy with the insecurities, anger, fear, and the almost inescapable feeling of being a disappointment, a failure, yet again. All the feelings that had once suffocated me as a young teen came rushing back again. The mask of bravado and confidence that I had put on for all these years had melted away to reveal the scared and unhappy little girl that remained inside me. I had escaped from this house, those feelings as soon as I was able to. Now, ten years later, it seems like very little had changed. Suffice to say, it was not a happy homecoming. It was a tragedy that had hurtled me back to my childhood home.

My aunt Liza had died. It still feels weird to say that out aloud. Aunty Liza is dead. I am still trying to wrap my head around the fact that this person who always seemed full to brim with life was no more. Even as she grew older, she seemed ready to take over the world, ready to embark upon another big adventure. Even though I had seen her lifeless body during the funeral, it was still hard for me to imagine her devoid of life and laughter. I had seen her just before her death. Cancer had whittled her away little by little till she was just skin and bones, and almost unrecognisable. Yet as she smiled upon seeing me, her face seemed to settle back into her old familiar warmth and the twinkle in her eye that always made you feel that you are the only one there who is in on her secret returned.

She had beckoned towards me, to come nearer and as I bent down to hear her better, she had whispered to me, conspiratorially, in her raspy voice, 'The garden snake. It is yours. It shall bring you all the luck in the world.' That was one of the last things aunty Liza had said to me. For the rest of my stay, she said little to me or anybody else. She just kindly smiled towards the hoard of relatives who cluttered the room, who had cared little for her throughout her life, but now hovered around her deathbed; almost vulture-like; keeping vigil till she died; hoping to claim a piece of the treasures she owned from around the world or the piece of land where she had built her home.

Aunty Liza, or rather my great aunt Liza, was the black sheep of the family. Youngest of my grandfather's siblings, she had forged her path at a time when the women in my family had little to no agency in choosing their future. She had run away with her dashing young neighbour when she was just eighteen. When the marriage fell apart, her family took her back but hardly let her forget the ignominy she had brought upon the family name. None the less, nothing seemed to put her down. She scrounged up money tutoring the neighbourhood children, put herself through college, and won a scholarship to a prestigious London college; thus, finally freeing herself from the chains that had held her down.

London was just the first step of her never-ending adventures. She hopped across the world; first as an intern to a bohemian writer, and then as a travel photographer and writer. All the while, her parents, siblings, and relatives tut-tutted her life choices, even as they boasted about their famed relation to strangers.

By the time I was born, she was at the peak of her career, travelling less for the need for money and more to satisfy her restless spirit. While I was bundled off to her home during the summers, she had chosen to retreat and rejuvenate at her home that she had bought just a few years before my birth. I had wondered why my parents kept on sending me back to her house to spend my days, even though their scorn for her was apparent. Perhaps it was to remind her of the few relations she still had, should she forget to add them in the will. I had always wondered why they had disliked her. Was it her boisterous laughter that echoed throughout the house? Her refusal to get married again, have children, or as they called it to 'settle down'? Perhaps it was her lovers who came in and out of her life, unable to keep up with her uncontainable energy and boundless spirit that craved knowledge and adventure. I had cheekily asked her about them once when I was almost sixteen. She had laughed and had said, "Oh! My five great loves and a few mistakes. Unfortunately, they all seemed to want too much of me for themselves." That was that. She never elaborated. I had never felt the need for any other explanation as well. To think of Aunty Liza being tied to someone, to give up pieces of herself to conform to the norms of relationships, was unthinkable.

Her home, with its vast gardens, was a place of happiness and freedom, in a way my own home was not. It was there, during those carefree summer days, that I had encountered the garden snake. It was nestled among the rose bushes. When I had first encountered it, playing some make-believe game as a child of six or seven, it had greatly perturbed me. It stood there, bright green with yellow spots and black eyes made of glass. It was just a statue, but it seemed as if it was ready to spring to life any minute. Those black glass eyes seemed depthless and appeared to hold secrets from the time before humans walked the earth. I had created a tiny little dance, which in my mind became a childish hex to ward off the evil spirit that I had once thought was contained within the statue of the yellow-speckled snake.

One day, upon curiously observing my elaborate ritual to avoid the statue in the garden, Aunty Liza had inquired about it. She stood listening to my childish fantasies, barely cracking a smile. As I finished my tale, she sighed and told me, "Oh hon! That statue does not contain any evil. However, you intuit well. It is an ancient relic." According to Aunt Liza, shrivelled old witch doctor had given it to her during her travels when she had helped and taken care of the old lady when she fell in a busy Turkish bazaar. The witch doctor had confided in her, recounting that she had fought an evil magician to win the statue. The statue of the garden snake is far from evil. It imparts those who hold it with good luck and the fulfillment of all their dreams.

She led me to it and held it in all earnestness with her eyes shut closed. "There," she said, "I have made my wish. Now it is your turn," as she handed it to me. It felt too heavy, too big, in my tiny child-like hand. I closed my eyes tight, imitating my aunt, and made a childish wish, long forgotten over time.

Since that day, the garden snake has been my comfort and companion. I went there when I was afraid of what the exam results would reveal, wished upon it to have the cute guy in my class to notice me, hoped that I stopped seeing the grotesque figure that I saw in the mirror, and wished for the courage to move out of my home.

Aunty Liza's story about its origins became more and more elaborate as time passed on. The evil magician had cheated a good, kindly king to rob him of it before it had reached the witch doctor. The good king had received it from a lady of the lake whom he had once saved from a cruel sea monster who had kept her a prisoner.

I returned to the statue the day after Aunty Liza's death. It had faded away in colour to reveal a brown body underneath it. The black glass eyes, however, remained as bright as ever. I picked it up from its resting place to bring it home with me.

Perhaps, rather than a mythical creature, it was just a thrift store buy. However, I held onto the hope that it was an ancient relic, fought over for centuries, imbued with magic to fulfill one's innermost dreams.

It now sits beside me on my bed table. I think it carries with it the spirit of my beloved aunt, along with the ancient spirit now. I hold it, closing my eyes hard, wishing away the insecurities of my childhood. Perhaps, it will also send me on adventures, revealing some new aspect of my identity. I hold it tighter, grasping to find inspiration from my aunt's lively and exhilarating life, hoping to find an escape from my loneliness and insecurities.

50

Mirage

by Komal R. D.

At first glance, Alice would seem rather a normal sixteen-year-old. Nothing in particular about her physical appearance was striking. She was a stout little teenager, with a chubby freckled face and bright red curly hair head. Moving and changing schools was a hard transition for Alice. Yet, she remained a favourite of most of her teachers but rather a victim of bullying at the hands of her classmates. She had changed multiple schools previously and now, she was in high school, which was a kind of a relief because she could not put up with her classmates anymore. She desperately sought to get out from the mess she was in. She was constantly bullied by her classmates in school about her size and her appearance. They hated her even before they laid eyes on her. It was like they had something against her in a past life. She did not hate being fat but disliked the fact that she was being ostracized for it. She was hoping despite everything, that there wouldn't be such monstrous bullies in her new school.

She put on a baggy sweatshirt that quoted "Cute but Psycho", well definitely psycho but far-away from being cute, she thought. She wore it with the only olive-green trousers she could fit in to. She tied her hair into a bun and cinched it with a bright red scarf. She had her shoelaces lazily tied around.

She was trying on her uniform for the start of the next academic year, accompanied by her mom and her two young brothers for shopping. Alice's mother was beautiful. She was tall with broad shoulders and an elegant waist. Where her mother was statuesque, Alice was hefty. Where her mother was fragile, Alice was smudged. After 3 kids, her mother still looked like she was competing for America's Next Top Model, while Alice at sixteen was already built like a tank. She had too much of everything and too little height to hide it. When her chin pushed against her neck, it made three fat chins. Her breasts started just below her chin and her hips were ridicule.

As she paced around the counters to find a matching plaid skirt for her newly selected shirt, she could hear the giggles and chuckles of two young girls at the next counter. She turned to have a look at them. She was stunned by their beauty. One of the girls had a sculpted figure. Her waist was tapered, and she had a burnish complexion. Her eyebrows were perfectly tweezed, and her eyelashes were long and velvety. Her sunrise gold hair plunged over her shoulders. The other girl was a few inches shorter than the first girl. She had her straight kohl-black hair pulled into a ponytail. She has a dainty nose and deep blue eyes. She had a rather cheerful personality. Looking at them made Alice immensely sad and she quickly went into the fitting room to evaluate her physique. Not one feature of her matched those of the pretty girls. Tears burst forth like water from a dam, spilling down her face. Perhaps, she was just chasing a mirage. She smudged her eyes, clenching the clothes to her chest, she barged out of the room, and asked her mom if they could go home soon.

On the way back home, the constant pestering of the two brothers made them stop at Dunkin donuts shop. Her mother reckoned that Alice was lost in her thoughts and decided to order her favourite, chocolate glazed donuts. She didn't talk to her mother, she spent so much time thinking about those two girls that she did not have a count of how many donuts she gulped down without realizing and reminiscing its taste. She paid no attention to her brothers rhapsodizing about their brand new spiderman backpacks.

That evening, she lay on her flabby stomach and started reading a 'Fangirl' book. Physically, she was present in her dingy room but mentally she was still at the shop gazing at the girls. She could not fathom how girls of her age looked so flawless while she was something of a comical character to the people around her. She loathed them or rather, she was jealous of what they had, and it was evident to her that she could never possess any of it. She hated herself for being so bothered about the way she looked. She started questioning her existence 'Why can't I dress like that? And act like that? Did I even inherit any good genes from my mother?' Yet, there were no answers to her inane questions. Every bully, every absurd comment, every name she was called, came back to her, like a boomerang. She felt suffocated and wanted to drown in the sea. Her eyes welled up with tears, an endless stream of feelings flowed down, and she broke down like never before. Tears had drained everything out of her and beneath, she buried her angst, her feelings. Alice did not know what to do anymore. She felt like a huge boulder had fallen on her and she was crushed beneath it, unable to move. She knew that other people had it much worse than her but she could not help but think about how miserable her life had become.

Well, people say that looks and appearances do not matter but it has always played a huge role in Alice's life and the way she has always been treated by the people around her. It never registered to Alice that she did exceedingly well in her academics or that she was a kind, sweet person. But alas, that is how human beings are, right? We never appreciate what we have right before us, but rather, we choose to whine about all that is missing from our lives, all that we cannot possess. Without pain, how could we know joy? Without darkness, how could we see light? We are all flawed in some way. Yet, we try to make amends with our flawed selves. If the world were full of perfect people, we would still be envious of the most perfect person and still feel bad about it.

Alice cried and cried until she fell asleep. She left her wounds open for the moon to heal and purify. The warm ball of light filtered through her thin eyelids awoke her. Rays of sunshine cast squares on the glossy floor, reflecting onto several objects in her room. She blinked a few times, to help her adjust to the illumination directed right at her defenceless figure. Just like any other morning, she lay on her bed motionless just staring at nothing in particular. She bent across her bed and swayed her hand to get hold of her morning coffee on the desk adjacent to her bed. But she caught hold of the coaster instead of a steaming hot cup of brewed coffee, which was quite unusual because her mother never missed her coffee. She pulled a band out to pull her hair into a ponytail. With the touch, she realized her hair was not frizzy or messy anymore. Her fingers felt smooth running through her hair. Not knowing what had happened, Alice jumped up from her bed with a jolt and ran towards the long mirror. She was flabbergasted to see herself transformed into a striking figure. Her chubby freckled face was now clear and radiant without a discernible spot. Her mercury red hair felt lustrous and silky. Her overly sized hips have taken a curvilinear shape of her waist. Her excess weight just reduced to a minuscule. She looked taller than usual, maybe height was a bonus. She beamed like a tube light and nothing stopped her ear-to-ear smile. Her happiness knew no bounds. She was dancing to the tune playing inside her head. Happiness was in the rain, ready to get drenched. It was in the beachy sunshine, to let the waves carry you. It was in the earthy flavour, a burst of aroma with each cut. Everything felt hazy and she kept looking at herself, again and again, to just admire how beautiful she looks. Looking at the mirror gave her an inner glow. She couldn't wait for her mother to look at her beautiful Alice. She could finally use the phrase "Like mother, like daughter", she thought. She could not stop giggling to herself. She bound down the stairs, missing a few steps in between, being careful not to let her brand-new self-get wounded. Alice called out to her mother, there wasn't any reply from the other side. She searched in the bedroom and kitchen. There was no sight of her mother or her two little brothers. Usually, her brothers run up and down the house, completely wrecking it. But this silence was unbearable. She felt worried and sat in the dining with her face in her hands. There was a letter lying next to her. Her stomach rumbled and she started sweating profusely. She held the letter and opened it slowly with trembling hands. It was a short note written in all caps. She saw her name ALICE written on it, cold sweat glistened on her brow. She clasped the letter tightly and read it aloud.

Dear Alice,

Welcome to your wonderland. You must be loving your new appearance but as you can see, it comes with a price. The price of being invisible to your loved ones and only visible to the outside world. Your mother and brothers are right here under this roof but neither of you can see each other.

Alice let out a loud cry. There was something in that cry, a pain behind it. She felt a pressure built inside like a ticking bomb, she needed to let it explode and get burnt to ashes with it. She started breathing heavily, breath was spilling out of her damaged lungs and she felt doomed. She had no control over her grief, she lay on her knees on the floor, with the letter still clenched tightly in her hands. She was frozen, unable to fathom what she just read. She closed her eyes and was still shedding tears. The whole world collapsed in front of her. She could never imagine her life without her family and remain the gorgeous girl in high school. This was not a price worth paying for. She heard a faint shout, her mother yelling "GET UP ALICE, TIME FOR SCHOOL". Alice was paralyzed with shock; she woke up in her bed realizing that it was all a very horrific dream. Her mother entered her room with her morning coffee, and emotional Alice hugged her mother and kept weeping in her mother's bosom. Her mother caressed her messy curly hair gently and laid a kiss on her forehead. From then on, Alice carried so much love for herself in her heart. She chooses to be kind, loving, and happy rather than having a magnificent figure. Each day, she was grateful for having such a supporting family and accepting the way she is and loving her unconditionally. Alice was back to being her same old self, but she was happy being the wrecked version of Alice from "ALICE IN THE WONDERLAND".

51

The Thing That Nobody Talks About

by Sushree Diya Om

I was diagnosed with different mental illnesses, including borderline personality disorder, bipolar disorder, PTSD, depression...'

For centuries, enlightened beings have spoken implicitly about the spiritual path and its many hurdles — our thoughts, our desires, distractions, our lingering emotions of anger and covetousness, and so forth. But there is one hurdle, the biggest of them all in my personal experience, that much light hasn't been shed upon from the perspective of a spiritual seeker.

I'd assume because the majority of sincere seekers and enlightened beings in the past have been male or it's been a topic that most people are not exactly comfortable discussing openly.

We all have our fair share of problems in life that we see as hurdles on the spiritual path: other people are a problem; money is a problem, for some people, health is a problem. And if we're going deeper, many of us are simply trying to stay afloat, treading water against the weight of our past traumas, losses, abuse, mental illness, and some unthinkable atrocities that can and have happened.

I am no stranger to any of the above. I am one, just like many of you, who is simply trying to stay afloat. Perhaps, one day in the future, I shall write more about them, but today is not that day.

Today, I wanted to write about this huge, lifelong hurdle that I've been dealing with. A struggle that is more debilitating and derailing than anything else I've had to deal with.

What can be bigger than anything I've listed thus far and yet still not be widely talked about in spirituality?

If you're a woman, you're very likely to know what I'm talking about, and if you're a man who lives in close quarters to a woman or has grown-up daughters, then you're going to be nodding your heads reading this one.

Got it yet? Female Hormones! Periods!

Growing up, most teenagers hit that grumpy stage where their hormones are raging, their once idolised parents have now become the mortal enemy. The ceremonial blurting out of, "I hate you!" to at least one unsuspecting parent who only asked if you wanted cereal for breakfast (sorry, Mum and Dad!) marks the rite of passage into this special time of 'kidulthood'. (Not an original phrase. It's from the title of the 2006 British film, Kidulthood.)

The teen suffers that internal crisis. Self-conscious, self-critical, not quite understanding their place in the world; a barrage of foreign, tumultuous feelings take siege over their once tranquil ship. Weird things are going on in their body, energy levels are all over the place, and a monkey-on-Red-Bull's tree acrobatics pale in comparison to their mood swings. (I can't remember exactly where I read it but I think this lovely monkey image is credited to Swami ji). And to top it off, the girl or boy they fancy at school, doesn't fancy them back, and worse still, they embarrassed themselves in front of the whole class. It feels like the end of the world. An utterly, utterly hopeless state.

Now, imagine this state of mind recurring almost every four weeks, for the rest of your life until around you're in your 50s. Yep, welcome to my world.

Three out of four women are said to suffer from some symptoms of Pre-Menstrual Stress/Tension (PMS/PMT). These would include an emotional state in varying degrees similar to that mentioned above, plus usually some physical symptoms such as bloating, fatigue, and all manner of digestive issues, aches, and pains. These symptoms usually alleviate once the period has started, although the cramps can last for a few more days.

If the symptoms are more severe and hinder a woman from carrying out her normal daily activities, it is called Pre-Menstrual Dysphoric Disorder (PMDD). There are different statistics about PMDD. It is said that 1 in 20 women of reproductive age are affected by it. I now know that I fall into this category.

As a young teen, I remember that I would feel intense emotions where I'd break down crying for no reason and my poor brother would ask me what was wrong and I'd cry out, "I don't know!" Or he'd say the wrong thing on a wrong day and I'd suddenly fall to the floor in a heap of tears and scream at him, "Get out!" (Sorry, Mish!).

I'd usually start my period within a day or two of feeling like that and then I'd feel so energised, alive, and probably quite annoyingly happy. I'd talk at a million miles an hour, I'd put on music and dance, or I'd sing at the top of my lungs disturbing everyone else's peace (again, sorry, Mish!). I felt so happy that I couldn't contain it. Then I'd plateau the next day and go back to my normal, bearable self for the next three weeks or so until the cycle started all over again.

I didn't fully understand then what was happening. And most boys in school joked about menstruation casually. If a girl didn't smile, one would hear, "You on your period or what?!" Periods were shrouded in stigma and mystery. Anyone I did speak to about it told me that it was normal, that it was just PMS, that most women go through it.

I ploughed through the first four years of my kidulthood believing the same. Only for me, it wasn't the same.

At the age of 15, I was hospitalised after the first of several attempts to take my own life. I had suffered some childhood traumas and the emotions I felt every month were so extreme that I couldn't handle them. I didn't want to live like that anymore.

In my 20s and 30s, I was diagnosed with different mental illnesses including borderline personality disorder, bipolar disorder, PTSD, and different types of depression. To this day, I don't know if these diagnoses were valid or not, I only know how I felt then and how I feel now.

At the age of 16, I moved out of the only home I'd ever known and away from the only people who loved me. I left school after my GCSE's, got a Christmas job at a retail shop, and moved into a bedsit on top of a video-rental library and fish 'n' chip shop, for £50 per week. To say my life since then has been onerous is an understatement.

(I've never been able to hold down a job for very long and I've never been in a stable relationship. I moved home around 20 times after that. I went back to my studies at the age of 23. It took me 8 years to get my law degree, working part-time. But, hey, I did it!)

25 years after first stepping into the world alone, after finding my Guru, Om Swami ji, after learning how to live a *sattvic* life, after a couple of thousand hours of meditation, after spending months at a time in solitude, I was finally able to handle my emotions a lot better; I mended my relationship with my family, I moved on from my past traumas, I was genuinely able to forgive my abusers and myself.

After some disastrously failed attempts, I remember my last stint in solitude where I was finally able to revel in a silent mind and take a dip into a state of bliss. I thought I was finally healed. I thought this feeling would last forever.

Wishful thinking? Well not entirely.

It is true that I no longer experienced the same helpless, suicidal thoughts, mental instability, or intense emotions like before, but I also noticed that I'd go through phases when I would feel like withdrawing to my room and I had no focus or energy, not even to read or meditate, let alone work outdoors in the ashram.

I used to love scrubbing down the cowshed or cleaning the ashram grounds. Sweeping and mopping floors and making things shiny was a joy! I wasn't content until I knew that the Lord's home was squeaky clean for Him.

During the down phases, however, I couldn't do anything. I could just about maintain my meditative state and my mind was relatively quiet, but physically, my body wouldn't cooperate. And soon the stretch of the down phases became longer and longer.

I was in pretty good health, I ate well and slept well so I couldn't understand what was wrong. Realising there was a pattern to my behaviour, I began to keep a diary of my up and down days concerning my monthly cycle.

Throughout the last couple of years, I noticed the duration of my PMS/PMDD symptoms began to increase from a few days before my period, to a week before, then up to two weeks before. Plus, the intensity, flow, and pain of my periods severely increased. I saw a gynaecologist. I was very anaemic — weak all the time because of the amount of blood loss. I had to start taking medication every month and increase my iron and supplement intake.

So just when I thought I was handling it, I realised, Mother Nature had thrown Perimenopause at me. (Well, I had been fervently praying to Her for early menopause so I could be free of my hormones. It looks like She heard me. Thanks, Ma!)

As I described it to someone recently, PMS/PMDD + Perimenopause = Kaboom!

It feels like having a mental illness and chronic fatigue syndrome 50-75% of the month and then being free of it only to have it happen again the following month.

However, if I feel like crying now, it usually isn't in any negative emotion anymore. I cry intensely in gratitude. I am aware that it is hormonal crying, and it is just as intense as always, but it is in a deeply positive emotion these days.

Other than that, I simply have to rest it out. Some days, I am so exhausted that I sleep all day, or I have such brain fog that I can't do much more than zone out on YouTube or Netflix (as mindfully as possible, of course).

It is entirely embarrassing for me to admit that I, a resident disciple of Om Swami, behave in this way. It's an old pattern, I'm yet to break, of binge-watching TV to block out how I'm feeling at the time. The guilt of doing this sometimes eats me up and affects me just as much as the hormones. But I guess,

I'm no longer subjecting myself to any self-destructive behaviour. This is massive progress.

Writing this post is a big step towards wholly accepting that it is what it is, that no matter how much I wish it, I cannot function at full capacity 100% of the time.

All I can do is my best, remain mindful of my thoughts and speech, and no matter how I am feeling on the inside, I must always, always, always be kind to others.

If I can't do much in terms of set *sadhanas*, and I want to continue to walk the spiritual path, I must not veer from these commandments to myself. It might take me longer to purify myself, but I shall not give up.

Over the years, I have tried every remedy, natural and allopathic. I have made all the recommended lifestyle changes. Only with Swami ji's grace and by following His teachings am I as stable as I am now. And although I am much, much better, I have accepted that perhaps, until I turn into a lovely, ol' wrinkly lady, this will be my biggest remaining hurdle on the path (a hysterectomy is not an option for me right now).

The silver lining, before my silver-grey hairs come in, is that every single month on the day after the down phase passes, I get to feel re-born again!

It's the most incredible feeling.

I appreciate every little thing so much! The sweet tastes so much sweeter after one has just digested the bitter. I taste it every month and today is a sweet, sweet day. I'm super-energised. I meditated, I did some of the work I had to do, I performed some acts of kindness, I've spring cleaned my room and my refrigerator, and I've written this post.

From tomorrow, I'll be back in the gym and yoga class, I'll brush the cows, I'll be responding to emails and comments on my previous posts (sorry for the delay!), I'll be back to my creative writing, singing and art practice, and my languages (I'm learning French, Italian, Japanese and Hindi). I try to make up for the lost time. I do as much as I can because I know the wheel will turn again, and that's okay. It is what it is.

So, to my PMS/PMT, PMDD hormonal, menopausal, borderline, bipolar, depressed, trauma survivor sisters and brothers out there, or anyone with similar symptoms, you are not alone! To think about it, we make up most of the population.

If you don't feel okay with yourself:

- Seek help
- Talk about it with people you trust.
- If you've been given a diagnosis, learn everything about it, and learn everything about yourself. Get to know yourself.
- Try to spot any patterns or specific triggers.
- It's okay to take medication if you need it, especially if your symptoms are more psychiatric.
- Most importantly, take care of your physical health and wellbeing, nobody else can do that for you.
- Be grateful for all the things in life that you usually might take for granted.
- Above all be grateful for every moment of clarity. They will come and go, but don't dwell on the negatives when God has blessed you with a good day.

- Seriously getting into meditation helped me. Along with my faith in God and my Guru, Om Swami ji, maintaining a meditative state at all times is my absolute anchor.
- If you're serious about managing your emotions, Om Swami ji's blog posts on os.me, His videos and books have all the information you'll ever need. They are how I finally learned to manage myself.

It takes work and it takes time. I'm 5 years in on this journey and although I am not quite where I could be, I know I am a different person from who I was before I read Swami ji's works. If I keep working on myself, hormones, or no hormones, I can only get better and better. I only wish that, many years ago, I knew what I know now!

And to those of you reading this who live in the same house with people like us, even if you live with someone who has very normal PMS/PMT symptoms, maybe your little daughters are growing up or your partner is just hitting menopause — please do the same — get as much information as possible, so you know how to support them in the way they need it.

Being around people who have not yet learned to manage their emotions can be stressful at the best of times, so understanding your loved ones' emotional/mental state and understanding how to keep yourself calm and healthy are just as important as each other.

Please take care of yourselves and each other.

Jai Sri Hari!

(Originally published as a post on os.me on October 17, 2020)

52

She Is Not Perfect, But Good Enough

by Munmun Aidasani

She doesn't need anyone's affection or approval to be good enough. Her worth is not contingent upon other people's acceptance ---it's something inherent. She exists and therefore She matters. She is allowed to voice her thoughts and feelings. She is allowed to assert her needs and take up space. If someone judges her, it's not actually about her, it's about them and their insecurities, limitations, and needs. She is allowed to remove anyone from her life who makes her feel otherwise.

She is no one else, but one among us. Have you ever felt that you've lost yourself or your identity? Have you ever felt that, will I be more than a mom ever again? It happens to me most of the time.

Sometimes I feel sorry for myself that I doubted my worth. I didn't realize how strong and how resilient I could be. Whenever I am alone, I converse with my loneliness that I don't need any sort of motivation or inspiration to start wheeling my journey again. I have to believe that I am a beautiful soul I may not be perfect, but I am good enough. I am like sunshine which appears with a streak. I am like the birds in the sky who fly far with their wings. I am like the moonlight on a night that does not want to fade. I am like a beautiful flower that blooms up in the spring.

The upbringing of normal Indian society is that men do not proactively do the household chores as instinctively as the lady of the house does. Our mind is set from the beginning and this thought is imbibed within us. But I wonder why a lady is always supposed to ask for help, both men and women are equally responsible for all the family chores.

Why She only has to shatter her dreams to balance her life? Why cannot she follow her passion? Why is She always judged by society and everyone else around? Why is She supposed to be at home and look after kids and other members alone? Why She has to face a lot of hurdles every day? Why She feels hard on the grounds of reality? Why is She completely directionless and headless? Why is She the source of fun for others which in turn causes havoc in her life? Why She has to feel that deep sense of guilt if She prioritizes something that interests her? Why She always has to make a choice? Why Her life is like peeling an onion, with every layer she opens, she shed her silent tears? Why with every sarcastic remark or injustice she has to move on?

There should always be a mutual understanding and equal distribution.

Rediscovering herself after motherhood and to mould herself at any point in time, it's like a battle which she has to conquer. She has to learn to prioritize herself so that she can be enough for her family but mostly for herself. She has to take the risk even though she is petrified of failures because she has to believe that her faith is stronger than her fear. Whenever life knocks her down, her only option is to stand back up and just wish that things would get better.

BEYOND THE POINT, She has to believe that real happiness comes from within, and to become complete, She has to feel enough with all her flaws and failures, with all her mistakes and imperfections. She is a life-giver. She is a creator. She is the one who can make four walls into a home. She has to believe that like her there can be no other. She is the one who can perfectly play any role. She needs no validation to feel valued and is the real form of contentment that She is good enough.

UPHILL
CLIMB

53

St(R)Ung Pearls

Who is at fault?
I wondered was it you or me? Neither,
just one unsaid thing
(Perhaps being beholden to me has been the undoing of the situation.)
Again, something that you and I knew
was what was intended
Yet as it was not spoken out
Did someone cast the evil eye on
our enviable relationship of decades? Now alas
we live in the shambles of silence and forced affection
and affectation!
Most grievous that it has happened at
this auspicious time
At the juncture of a new relationship
An old cherished one has shown cracks
That were never known to have
existed.
Woman that I am
With oyster-like effort I shall strive to
Prove it is not what you think
I shall put this grain of sorrow aside
Layer it with words and deeds
To hopefully shape a pearl

That you may accept to commemorate a misunderstanding.

by Renee Mary Jetto

54

Getting Closer

You are getting into the crevices now.
The mirror is so close, at all angles.
There is nowhere to hide.
Because
the entire room is made of mirrors now. And what I see
is a reflection.
Like feathers floating in the breeze, they go by.
Sometimes a moment is frozen.
Random but intelligently, precisely, perfect.
How great are you.
How to love you?
it just doesn't seem possible.
Because you don't need it.
But I still do.

by Christine J.

55

Loving Your Memory

I inhale your skin,
I touch every pore,
I move my fingers over every curve,
Every bend of your bone,
I linger more,
Like I have never lingered before
Loving your memory becomes more beautiful every day

by Baishakhi Mukherjee

56

A Proud Flower

Hey! that's not me.
You're mistaken!
I might resemble one
But not the one you thought.

I'm a proud flower
that bloomed to spread joy,
freshen up the air and
fall off before the night is out.

I'm sorry that I have a face,
I do have my limbs, but
not really I'm a human; 'coz
I'm ashamed to be one.

by Maria Mappilassery

57

Insane Love

The guileless zest of childhood has faded
Or is it dancing deep within me ?
Bobbing up
every now and then
In surge and spurts and sublime hues.

I still see Spring waiting in the wings
Hued wonders rearing to reveal.
Turning heads and those craving looks
Reigning beauty in fullest bloom.

The blossom of buds still resplendent
Naked under the leaves of green
With passion and colour overflowing
Till breath transports to another space.

Those Tiny wrinkles
my soulmates loyal
The sprinkling of snow that has fallen
As I stand besotted with this Fall
Pronto... tomorrows turn into yesterdays !

I sit here
in touch with this morn
Taken over by this fiery energy cascading

Escorting me to get away with million
Glorious laughs and revelry in abundance !

LIFE.
To my tunes
I made you dance tirelessly
Wrapped you round my little finger
The games we played were oh so challenging
Beckoning...trapping... freeing... embracing.

Tightly I hold you, closer to my chest
As lyrics of a song, pictures of a memory
With the glee of a child, filling my smile
I realise you are nothing, but
Insane love!

by Nalini Vipin

58

Souls for the Bodies

A woman with a soul met a man with a body
Neither the man saw her soul nor she saw his body.
The man loved her body; may be more than he loved his
own
His wishes won over her whilst she searched frantically for
his soul,
in a hope that the souls could meet each other one day.
Little did she know that her search was in vain.
And it was time for another girl to be born with a soul,
Yet another boy was born somewhere with a body too.
This was normal, a cycle that everyone knew since life
existed.
Oh! How lucky are those bodies to be corporeal;
Whilst the poor souls weren't quite sure if they existed for
real.

by Maria Mappilassery

59

Old Friends

Old friends of mine,
Came over to say 'Hi'.
I could hardly recognise them.
And I sensed my neglect in their timidness,
In the uncertainty they had of my welcome.
As my recognition dawned on them,
They started to glow and grow.
And as I saw how my acknowledgement,
Fed their confidence,
I felt their hurt and sadness as my own.
But they beam at me with no judgement,
I feel my guilt, my shame...
I feel a resolve to treat them better...

Old dreams came over to pay me a visit,
I wonder if I'll give them a chance this time...

by Padma

60

Love Story – Trash And Bin

She said "Love her, like her father did"
He said "He needs to think"
She said "I love you"
He said "He needs time"
She said "I am madly in love"
He said "I don't understand"
She asked "Would you re-think"
He said "Read Between the Lines"
She said "I believe you"
He said "I don't have belief in you"
She said "I care for you"
He said "You are an Angel"
She said "I am always extreme"
He said "He will use the cane"
She said "I am a trash"
He said "He has made some trash"
She said "She will talk"
He said "He will try"
She said "It's a deal"
He said "I agree to the deal"
She said "I would be thrown"
He said "He will be gone"
She said "She is happy"
He said "He is lucky"
She said "I miss you"

He said "Sorry...Gotta go"
She said "I love you"
He said "I gave you hope"
She asked when he would go
He asked when she would meet
She said "I am gonna go"
He said "He does not like"
She said "I am missing you"
He said "You don't mean a word"
She said "I want to talk"
He said "This is not the time"
She said "I am thinking of you"
He said "You are only drunk"
She said "I meant all i said"
He said "I have no time for what you said"
She said "You were in my mind"
He said "Add it to her book"
She said "I miss u a lot"
He said "He wants to sleep"

She didn't say that she was feeling vacuum
She didn't say that she is not happy with the deal
She didn't say how she felt about him
She didn't say she meant all she said
She didn't Say why she's a trash
She didn't say she didn't want him to go
She didn't say he is the music of her life
She didn't say he has become the reason for her to live
She didn't say she wanted him lifelong
She didn't say she cried whole day long
She didn't Say she had been bleeding for some time long

But then all she said was that she loves him a Lot... but then would never ever come back to hurt him in anyway

He said,
"Sick of crying, tired of trying, yeah am smiling, but inside I am dying
I told you to lie next to me and you smiled and said "I love you"
You can tell me you love me
You can tell me you care
but I can never trust you
No, not again
but now I know the truth
you loved me never
50% angel... 50% evil... and that's you...my baby dear"

And she said for the very last time "I love you
You will realize
But then it will be too late."

by Divya Naveen

61

A Beautiful Struggle

by Joshuanna Woods

Dear God,

My King, My Father, My Friend, My Guide, My All...

You know my heart. You hold my future. You hold my life. Continue to mould me & construct me into your warrior. Encourage me when I just need to hear a word, lift me when I'm feeling down, hold me when I feel like I'm all alone, and love me when I feel no one does.

Feb 16, 2011

Growing up everyone is thrilled by the thought of growing up. Depending on what guidance was provided, some more eager than others. I was one of those eager individuals. Ready to jump into the world I knew little of; yet life had granted me many struggles already, how could adulthood be any worse? Well, it was not until I was in my mid-twenties with 4 children under 8 and anticipating the divorce that I realized how deep and unguided I was. It was then that I realized I was not prepared. See, no one prepared you for real-life after 18. They give you sugar-coated facts on life, love, and finding success. They don't tell you the downfalls and what you have to overcome that makes life so meaningful. Why is the truth so hard to serve? Why is being honest and open such a scary thing?

I fell in love at 18, at least that what I thought love was. I accepted him and changed without question. I thought that's what the old love consisted of, unconditional love as you build to change each other's world. I had a previous child and had dropped out of school to work and support her. Yes, I had dreams; I wanted to travel the world. He accepted us both and provided for us as well as his nephew who looked up to him dearly. I admired his heart and his will. I love him even when everyone else sneered at his name. I saw him. We planned a future together and he took off to the military to set things in motion. I was grateful until the skeletons began to fall out of the closet. My vision was blurred. I was dazed by the man I loved, but I was committed to making it work so I stuck by it. I'd always been honest to him about my sexuality, but I didn't intend on hurting him with my confusion and blurred thoughts. I'd befriend a female that could relate to my situation. She had a son, and we began to spend time together. I intended to just be friends, but we found ourselves exploring shared pain. This weak moment became the pivotal point of our relations. To him it was betrayal but there was never a moment that this action wasn't welcome for him to be a part of. Our relationship swayed after this moment.

Shortly afterward, I too joined the military but reserves to be able to travel with him. I understood the betrayal after completing basic training but in life, you can only learn from your mistakes and move on. We swayed on and off for a year before I decided to move 3 states away and make life more official. We'd been talking for 2 years and only our family knew the details. To me, it was a bit insulting, and I understood his reasoning for protection, but my heart was not well with just that. My stay with him was just as depressed as our relationship over the past 2 years. There were bumps from self-respect to expectations swirled in lack of communication, from the pull in different directions because of work. Why didn't anyone tell you that loving someone while you're trying to grow individually takes so much work? Here I was lost in his life as mine dwindled in my thoughts. I was lost in a dream and didn't even know who I was!

Why wasn't I taught how to focus on me while loving him? I was so lost in him that I didn't realize I no longer loved him but the ideal we created together. After three months of living in entrapment, I planned to return home, but the kicker was… I was now pregnant with our first child together. Something we planned but I didn't expect it to happen then. I wanted to get things together. I wanted to be sure because we didn't plan a life together for us to raise the children separately. I was devastated but I couldn't live the way I had been.

Almost another year went by and I was expecting our son any day. We'd kept in contact on and off as my love for him continued to grow despite the pain I bore. I'd already lost my virginity unwillingly stripping me of my innocence. I lost my mother early depriving me of her guidance. Now the man I loved, and my dream life was on the edge of destruction. I hung on to us like life had no other option. The pending tear in my heart was crippling. Then one day he showed up and stepped up. He declared to be there for his son and never to leave us. He proposed after Christmas and I was shocked but said yes. He was an excellent coach during our son's birth and handled the aftercare like no other. I was amazed at his efforts. A few weeks later we wedded and the next month I was back 3 states away beginning life with him. At least, that's what I thought. I thought life would be better but when a person is in a comfortable situation and environment, they change. Why didn't anyone teach me the signs? Why was I so willing and eager for love? 3 months later and the nightmare began. I was accustomed to his drinking, but it was consuming his life. He was reckless and uncontrollable hiding from the world in distance. When I informed him that we were having another child, he was livid. Regardless of my lack of interaction with the world outside of the military, I was accustomed to having an affair. Shortly afterward I was left to fend for myself while he left for deployment. He still provided shelter and food, but life was a struggle with two children and a belly growing daily.

Needless to say, 8 months in I was fed up. I refused to deliver a child without knowing where my other children would go. So, I packed our things up with the help of his friend, not him, and moved back home. I was livid at this moment. This was not my dream. I didn't dream of living life alone, I felt alone in a relationship and money was not the issue. I do not care what people claim; money provides an opportunity; it does not make you happy. It CANNOT make you happy. It is important to connect and grow in life. Having funds to do things you dream of with people or to meet people makes life meaningful. We are creatures who were meant to connect. My water ended up breaking while I was home alone. Everyone was out of town and the local hospital turned me away claiming false labour. I was livid. Although advised not to, I drove 45 minutes away and was checked into labour and delivery. I begged and pleaded for him to be there but once he was, I wished he never came. I was in labour for 18 hours, pending an emergency c-section, before my problem child decided to peek into the world while I was sitting in a rocking chair. Again, I pleaded for him and he overlooked my pain, which became a common issue. My third child and our second entered the world as the doctor rushed into the room. Something should have told me then that life was going to be hell, but my heart still held on to the dream that was set.

He was home for a few months before another deployment and I counted the months of being sexually inactive before and after his deployment. Was this what marriage was supposed to be? Did things like this happen in a committed relationship, or was this just happening to me? I mean I am very resilient but at this point did he even want me or was it a possessive thing? I know the catch that I am but not sure if I want to be caught if this is what happiness contains. I was done. My heart had officially let go, now I was battling with my mind. Why doesn't anybody educate you on these things? Teach you to learn to trust yourself (mind, body, soul, and guts) and make the best decision that fits your life, not necessarily your desires. I wanted out and at this point, logic was not considered. I stepped out. I created a ripple and converted back to old habits. I just needed a feeling. My feelings landed me pregnant, but it wasn't until I was over my rant and decided to hear him out that I realized. Here I was with this tremendous reason for him to leave and my heart couldn't keep it secret. It has always been important to be accepted, and if he couldn't accept me, I wasn't going to be in it. He accepted, but I rejected the terms. I could no longer live a life of partial lies. I couldn't just depend on love alone. So, I was replaced and eventually, that place for love left. Don't get me wrong, I still love him, but I love me more.

I began to love myself, unconditionally, noticing things I didn't notice before. At first, I cried days and nights for the dream I woke up from. I went through phases of worthlessness until one day I was tired of being tired. I took notes from the letters I reviewed what I wanted and began to set my standards. I started at a minimum wage job and worked my way up. When one thing began stressing me out, I began setting new goals and expectations. I began to speak about the life I desired. As of today, I am still a work in progress, but I am proud to say, "I AM MORE THAN JUST A CONQUEROR!" I have created new standards for my children to be raised on and encourage them to be more than I am today. I encourage my surroundings to step back and take a long look at themselves and their desires before running into a life of dreams. It's not the dreams that are the problem, but the preparations we've done to transform them into reality.

62

The Woman Is The Village

by Soumya Gudiyella

It was the year 2020; the year COVID-19 changed our lives and forced a new normal on us.

I was in front of my iPad, and with excitement, I clicked the hangouts video button. I was meeting my long-lost friends virtually. About ten years ago, we lived under the same roof, while we pursued higher education in the United States. Our early adulthood dreams of finding a job and a life partner seemed trivial when compared to our current responsibilities.

My friends started popping up on the screen, the curly-haired Maya, calm Anu, friendly Geetha, and vivacious Kareena. All of us said, hello at once and for a couple of seconds, nobody could understand what the other person was saying. All of us looked older, our features were no longer refined because it bore the mark of motherhood, every sleepless night etched into our faces. We were happy to look at one another. Time and distance melted away, we were both young adults and mothers at once. We spoke about our kids, who ranged from new-borns and toddlers to middle school kids and enquired about the well-being of our families.

The topic of the call was, 'How are we coping with the COVID-19 lockdown? What are we doing to keep ourselves sane in this uncertain world?'

Maya asked, 'Do you feel that there is an increase in domestic chores after the pandemic? Cooking, cleaning, and washing clothes and dishes, taking care of the food requirements of the whole family rests on our shoulders. Nothing happens at home if we are not working. On top of it, we also have to work from home, with no childcare support, no day-cares, and no nannies. It is wearing me down.'

I agreed and said, 'It is almost like society decided cooking, cleaning, taking care of children is a woman's job. Women wanted to earn their living, which society allowed, but it also reminds us not to forget the tasks at home. They are still a woman's job. Anu and Geetha nodded their heads as Maya, and I vented our frustrations.

I added that 'I am tired about the duplicity, where women behave as though everything is perfect in their lives. How are you doing? I am fine. Why don't you tell the truth? I am bone tired wiping the same spot on the floor, standing in front of the sizzling curry for the hundredth time or scraping those stubborn dishes, for the thousandth time.'

Maya interrupted saying, 'Puja, I agree to all of that, but what should we do to keep our sanity? When the tasks keep piling up and we have minimal support from our family. How do we get that 'me' time to rejuvenate ourselves?'

Maya answered the question first by asking, 'Do you know about skiving?'

When we replied by saying 'no', Maya continued, 'Skiving is taking off from work, not letting your family members know, and spending the day as you desire. For example, I took a day off and did not tell my husband and mother-in-law. I took a long shower, read a book, and caught up on sleep.'

Kareena added, 'I did that before COVID-19. I left the office early, grabbed a coffee, and roamed around the mall before I picked the kids from school. A little bit of 'me' time every week.'

I interjected saying, 'Even my mom suggested something like that, but I am too sincere. Last December, I went to the Panera Bread restaurant to have a long lunch while I enjoyed the company of a book, but I told my husband later.'

My friends tutted and said, 'The point of skiving is not to tell your family.'

Geetha added with a smile, 'I did something like that, but it was to complete training so that I don't miss the deadline. I couldn't complete it without taking the day off. After work, my day was busy with taking care of an infant and a toddler.'

Geetha continued, 'My in-laws are here for almost six months due to the COVID-19, they couldn't fly back to India. They feel trapped and they take out their frustrations on me. They expect me to cook three meals every day and also take care of all the household chores. Before COVID-19, the toddler went to day-care and I went to the office. I had some break. Now, all of us are at home and I feel judged all the time. The insinuations are only for me, my husband doesn't even know. One day, I broke down in front of my husband, and since then we split the chores at home. I decided to cook only once per day. I started going for long walks around the neighbourhood with my kids. That way, I can get out from home for at least an hour every day.'

I agreed with Geetha and said, 'It is tough when the in-laws are at home. I faced a similar situation with my daughter when she was six months old. I was tired of taking care of my daughter and all the household responsibilities, cooking, cleaning, and also going to work. One day, I wanted to take my car and disappear for the whole day without letting anybody know about my whereabouts. It took a lot of restraint not to do that. I started doing yoga and that has calmed me.'

Anu revealed that she felt burdened just the same as all of us. She said, 'Sometimes, I feel so tired that I snap at my husband and kids. These days, I ask my husband to take my daughters for a walk. They are all gone for an hour or so. I use this time to listen to some music, watch something on Netflix or just sip some hot tea leisurely. I make it a point not to do any household chores in that one hour, it is my time to unwind.'

Maya joined and said, 'Yes, I feel myself break down too; the important thing is to understand what triggers it and do something beforehand. I go for a long bath, with scented candles.'

Kareena added, 'Taking care of the children or doing household tasks is not a one-time responsibility of the husbands. My husband and I share household tasks and taking care of children. I have the 100/80/50 rule. A few tasks need 100% of our attention, a few 50% and a few don't deserve our attention at all. Not everything on our plate has to be done in a day, it has to be prioritized. There are days when the dishes remain unwashed, and the house is a mess. So be it. The next day is always a new day and things are more in order. What is needed is having a sincere discussion with our partners about the things that we feel stressed about and figure out how to make it less stressful. It is the feeling of helplessness that creates trouble.

Recently, I saw a Facebook video about life lessons. In that video, they boiled both potatoes and eggs. The potatoes are hard, but they become soft after they are cooked. The eggs are fragile, but they become hard after they are cooked. The situations in life will always put us in hot water. It is up to us whether we become soft, empathize with others, and take action or if we become hard, blame others and do nothing. We always have the power to choose and set things right. It might be a difficult path for a few of us, but don't feel helpless.'

Kareena has been a mother long before us and she learned a few life hacks. The rest of us were in the throes of motherhood and COVID-19 has made our lives more difficult without the external support to take care of the kids. It is said that we need a village to raise a child. The woman is the village now. She is forced to play multiple roles and given little time to rest and recover.

We all felt that someone was piling huge stones on our shoulders. As we improved our stamina, they piled more and more. We have to put that burden aside, do whatever is needed to soothe those aching shoulders, and then lift only the ones that are necessary to get by the day.

Cries were heard in the background and someone called out the names of my friends. We dropped off one by one from the hangouts meeting. We were glad to have met and shared some tips and tricks to get through the COVID-19 motherhood situation. Society takes women and their role in motherhood and domesticity for granted. All we have is the support from our besties, which is like a cool shade in the scorching desert.

63

A Wink Of Sleep

by Tejasvi Rajesh

It was a hot and humid night in June. I lay in bed looking up at the ceiling fan, and each of its slow, heavy, noisy rotations. I had a long day, dashing across corridors in the Court Complex to present my case in different court halls, and after court hours, preparing documents for forthcoming cases, well past dinner time. It was 11 PM when I got home, and I was thankful for my colleagues who bought me dinner, and saved me from having to cook. I was as tired as one can be, and the thought of a good night's sleep appealed to me immensely.

My thoughts and happiness were short-lived, for I was unable to get a wink of sleep. A bat flapping its wings, an occasional motor vehicle horn, the sound of footsteps scuttling along the stairway outside my one-bedroomed flat. With each sound, I awoke, startled, scared of being alone and vulnerable. The heat of the day and the night left me feeling dehydrated. I stood up and slowly made my way to the water pot in the kitchen. It was 2 AM. I heard the leaves on the tree outside the gate swoosh and rustle in the gentle breeze. It took me down memory lane, an incident that I experienced almost a decade ago. I was a college-going girl at the time. I spent a beautiful evening with my closest girls, a gala dinner, and was walking back home. Familiar, yet unfamiliar streets welcomed me on my way home. My family was very protective of me when I was growing up. A girl is always vulnerable to the many dangers of the world. A girl is not to be out on the streets after dusk sets in. Suffocated. I felt suffocated all along, but when I went to college,

I felt a new form of energy surging through my body. Free and independent. Bold and young. I was ready to face the world, finally! But that night, I went back to my younger self, longing and hoping that I had my parents around me. I took the same path back to my PG, but I wasn't alone. Or so I felt. I heard the leaves on the trees rustle and woosh in the gentle breeze. I felt a pair of eyes keeping a tight watch on me. I heard footsteps. I felt the air around me change. Acid, I was able to smell acid. A parched throat and full stomach after a heavy meal. All I wanted to do was run home. A shiver down my spine. Buckling knees. My head spun. None of this stopped my tired legs from running as fast as they could, only to stop when I had entered my room and locked the door behind me. I didn't turn around to see if someone was following me on the street that night. All I know is that I craved for a wink of sleep that night.

Trying to push the memory aside, I walked back to my bed. I forced my brain not to think into it. I looked at the clock. It was 2:30 AM. I knew I had to squeeze in four hours of sleep, at least. I took a few deep breaths. I tried to calm down. I closed my eyes. A stray dog howled in the distance. I heard the wind woosh. I twisted and turned. I felt my knees buckle, just as they had all those years ago. I didn't have to run back home, it wasn't the same night. Only one fact remained- years later, I still craved for a wink of sleep.

64

That First Day Of My Life

by Vidya Shivaram

That first day of my life.

The first online experience - What was seen and what was experienced from an ordinary teacher's emotional journey. Here's what transpired on putting words to that which popped in the mind.

Today was my first experience of online classes in my career. My mind was rambling with a mix of numerous emotions all at once. The excitement of learning something new, a whole new spirit, some despair, a little anxiety, a bit of worry, sadness all this with a combination of confusion soaked and drenched me completely. I strongly felt a need to share this with you all, hence wrote these words.

A dreamer who left her village and moved towards the city with determination to earn a living - That is me. I didn't know anything else other than talking to people since childhood. So, it was a natural transition into the teaching profession where this became my strength. I also had another strong reason to choose this career. I'm an emotional person who is touched by the little things that life offers. Neither now, nor did I ever have the patience or will or interest to sit and work for hours in front of lifeless things.

Whatever, I had learnt to tread this path since a couple of years ago. I will write again about the ups and downs of my experience. But not even in my dreams did I think that I would see a day when I would sit at home and teach my students. And that too in a school like Prakriya.

Because this is one of the few Institutions which encourages children with Nature's wisdom and also that there is a life away from the internet, cell phones, and laptops. Given an opportunity, we warn children not to use these at least once a day. But today we are at a moment where we ask them to come to the screen every hour. This luxury was brought to us by our new friend Corona. Despite all the advances in technology and amazing discoveries happening outside, Prakriya did not allow any of these to compromise with her basic first principles.

Prakriya is one such place that believed in what it did and said it out loud and bold without any fear till now. It has never promised to teach its students competition but has assured to keep the spirit of child intact and teach him how to face life in the past and now, and so, will it in the future. Even to a school like ours which was a role model to many, Corona has brought in a situation where we have had to choose this online communication reluctantly.

Even if it's surprising, this is the truth that stands in front of us. The miracles and mystery of such a life, so small and so invisible itself are many. Imagine the mayhem if it were bigger and the eyes could see it. This fact often astonishes me

Today, May 6th was the beginning of a new Academic year. I didn't have to go to the first class of the first year at 8.30 am. But was sitting in front of my computer instead.

There was an orientation happening for the 10th Std. students. Even without stepping outside the house, I could see all the students and teachers on a single screen. I don't know whether to classify this as a luxury or bad luck. When I saw all the children in front of their systems holding the phone, I didn't know whether to praise or curse these inventions.

Every time someone spoke, I tried to find life on that lifeless and dull screen and failed. I remembered the words of a student who had said once upon a time in one of my classes. "I wish there were online classes, there wouldn't be any more traffic jams or pollution. It would be easy and safe. Also saves time". That day, though I did not agree with him completely, saw some truth in what he said. What a coincidence that such a situation has surfaced today where the entire world is available at our fingertips at the click of a button. Sitting inside 4 walls with an 8*13 screen in front of me and teaching felt like talking to walls. The kids have the option of shutting down their video. If they use this when we are taking classes, then even that opportunity is gone. Who knows if they want to listen to us or not!

For a person like me who can't sit in a place for more than 10 mins, sitting continuously for 2 hours in front of the computer got my back aching on the very first day. My eyes were hurting.

My ears were pleading to throw the earphones away. My legs were yelling at me "Enough, just stand and walk". I have never learnt the art of sitting in one place and teaching. But this situation is teaching me how to do it with no other option. Such a need has risen now. Also, there is a need to upgrade to a skill of remaining alert to multiple things happening at the same time. Phew!

The Internet seems to be the biggest enemy of online classes. It's even more harmful than Corona.

It goes off exactly at the time you need it. Even if you start the class with all preparation, once the network is down - the class is over. Even despite all these happenings, if I were to look at this situation positively, we need to learn and upgrade and keep ourselves involved. We need to be open to change. This is a new experience. New learning. Understanding the working of some new software tools.

But whatever one may say, let the world progress at its rapid rate, let there be a mystery, let there be miracles, discoveries, my personal opinion is that a student and teacher relationship is effective only face to face and in normal classrooms. Students and teachers are part of a school community. Whichever one element is absent; it becomes a building of stones and mud. The day a student and teacher stop meeting face to face and all education becomes online, that day in society we would have a bunch of robots with a lot of information and no feelings. I hope and pray that I don't have to see such a day!

65

June 14

by Sabhyata Bhandari

It was just another regular day!

A day full of work and fights and mental breakdowns.

To get everything off my chest, I called one of my closest friends. Talking to him made me feel comfortable, he never judged me for who I was and calmly listened to whatever I had to say. While engrossed in our chitchats and arguments, he suddenly popped the question, "I want to see how you used to look like before you became wheelchair-bound."

My heart sank for a second, not because he asked to see me but because I didn't remember what I used to look like, how I used to dress, how I used to behave, how I used to live before becoming wheelchair-bound, and most importantly, how I used to walk. I don't remember any of it at all.

What might have happened, you wonder?

June 14, 2012

A day that changed my whole life, a day when society labelled me as wheelchair-bound, a day when I became the person I never thought I would become.

“This girl is still sleeping,” my mom yelled.

“Wake up it’s 9:00 a.m. How can you sleep so much? C'mon, we have lots of work done. Go get ready.”

With a heavy heart and an annoying face, I woke up at last.

With the hustle and bustle of construction going on at our place, it was extremely hard for me to take another nap. So, I decided to go for a bath.

“See this palisade (aka jangla), it’s open, keep that in your mind. Don’t come near it,” explaining things to people around me, I went on to do my work.

“How much time are you going to take on?” my younger sister yelled.

“I just came in!” I replied.

“Do me a favour, let me take the bath first” my sister said.

“Please! I promise to pay you back.” She said.

“Alright but make it fast! Otherwise, mom is going to kill me.”

I came out of the room, explaining to my mom how my younger sister asked me to let her take a bath first. Talking to her, I tried to cross the palisade from a corner, and the next thing I know, everything went black!

I woke up with people yelling around me.

Pick up the girl.”

“What happened?”

They picked me up. The pain was extremely real, with me shouting and then a glance over my body and the only thing that came out of my mouth,

"Papa, my legs!"

I was immediately taken to the emergency care unit, where I was referred to another city.

"She won't be able to walk again!" said one of the doctors.

"You should buy her an automatic wheelchair," said another doctor.

"She will be dependent on you for the rest of her life," said another doctor to my parents.

Yes! JUNE 14, a day that changed my life, a day that made me a differently-abled person. A day that made me realise who my real friends were and a day that made me learn the facts of life that I wasn't ready for. A mere girl of 21 years, full of dreams, everything was taken away from her in a few seconds.

All these thoughts were running through my mind, and then my friend yelled,

"Hello! Madam so when can I expect to see you?" he said.

"Well! I don't have any picture of mine." I said

"Are you crazy? C'mon, I know that's a lie!" he said.

"No, frankly speaking, I don't have any pictures," I said with a sigh and cut the call.

While I put the phone down, I kept on wondering what sort of a person I was, how I used to look, how I used to walk. Why the hell don't I don't remember anything? Has it been this long? How many years? I asked myself. With a tear rolling down my eyes, my heart cried.

IT'S BEEN 8 YEARS!

66

Fortunes And Decisions

by Anju Anil

It was a Friday evening and Meera was driving back home from the office. It was past 9:00 pm and the vehicles in the front were moving at a snail's pace. A long weekend and a Friday evening are the perfect combination for the already infamous traffic on the Bangalore old airport road. She did not have to release the clutch for a long time and the car was moving in half clutch and first gear for the last 4 km stretch.

The vehicle finally reached the Kundalahalli traffic signal, one of the busiest signals in Bangalore. The signal turned green and there was a long queue of vehicles in the front. Before she could pass through the junction, the signal changed to red again. Meera has been working in the IT field in Bangalore for the last 15 years. She had recently been promoted as Operations Manager of a multinational firm. She was looking forward to the weekend to relax and recharge. She hoped she could cross the signal the second time as the traffic gained some momentum. She could see a family with 2 kids trying to cross the road at a distance. None of the cars were slowing down since everyone wanted to cover as much distance as possible before the next traffic block. Meera stopped the vehicle so that they could cross the road.

This incident took her 15 years back in time. She was so scared to cross a busy road. It was her best friend Priya who helped her cross the road during the first few days of Engineering college. The college was in front of a busy road, and they had to cross the road to reach the ladies' hostel. It was when Meera came to the City after she got admission to the engineering college. Priya was her roommate. Meera was born and brought up in a small village in South India in a middle-class family. Her father was a schoolteacher. He wanted her to pursue post-graduation and become a college lecturer. But Meera did not want to do a master's in science but wanted to do a professional course. She was always good in academics and securing a good job was her ambition from her early school days. She convinced her father to allow her to join the coaching class in a bigger town since there was no coaching facility in the town next to her village. She was fortunate as her father was willing to give her freedom of choice which was rare in many households during that time of the early years of the 21st century. Most parents were willing to encourage their sons to join professional courses and they wanted to make marriage arrangements soon after graduation for their daughters. Meera could secure a good rank in the entrance examination and get admission into one of the most prestigious engineering colleges.

Priya also joined the same college and had a similar background. Her father was a postmaster. Priya was very brilliant and attractive. Both of them got placed in good companies though different, during the final year of their program. Meera let out a deep sigh, it was almost 15 years since they met. The last day of their college life was as vivid in her memory as it was yesterday. Priya was about to join the training program of a major IT firm that recruited her. It was just after the final exams that Priya's father was diagnosed with 4th stage lung cancer. Doctors declared that chances were bleak and that he could hardly survive 4 more months. Priya's father wanted to see his daughter married before his last breath. On the last day of college, she gave the wedding invitation card to all her friends and invited everyone to attend her marriage. Though she was smiling, her eyes lost that sparkling. Meera could not congratulate her best friend as the sound choked in her throat. Priya's fiancé was her father's distant relative. He was a software engineer in the US and wanted to take his wife with him to the US post-marriage. Now she is a homemaker and is busy with two kids and helping them with their studies. She is also happy and confined within her family life. This was a very touching incident for Meera in her twenties. She always felt pained by the fact that her best friend had sacrificed all her dreams for her family. So, she decided that she would never sacrifice her goals and ambitions for marriage and to only marry a person who would allow her to continue pursuing her career and she was ready to wait. During marriage proposals to Meera, she had to decline a few of the proposals as the boy's job was in some other city /country and she had to leave her job to marry him.

There was pressure from relatives, but her father stood by her.

She is always grateful to her father who always supported his daughter to fulfill her dreams. He had to oppose many other close relatives who had advised him that marriage is always a better option for a girl child than a career as it was the normal practice in almost all families they know. At the same time, Meera also was determined and fought for many things that helped her in shaping up her future. At many times, there was the uncertainty of her future in her life, there was complete darkness, there were circumstances where she could have decided to choose marriage over a career like many of her role model intelligent girls - friends or cousin sisters - have done. While looking back through her journey, she firmly believes that she is in such a respectful position not only because she was fortunate but also because of her decisions and determination.

Meera's flashback stopped as she reached the apartment gate.

IN

ECLIPSE

67

Losing To The Other One

A cup broken and the saucer shattered, a few words spoke
A soul mate turned to a mundane partner,
A beautiful relationship became responsibilities and duties.
A wine glass in hand and miles of words in the starry night,
A beautiful pain stabbing the heart, waiting for the first "hi" on screen,
While someone tossed in bed for hours, alone.
A precious relationship taking birth, opening its eyes,
Beautiful, quivering in the breeze,
While another lay dying slowly
The day passes in to-do lists — milk, eggs, pulses, rice
For one these are the foundation bricks of a family,
The other waits for the night to be rid of the mundane and slip into the misty land
When did the dream break?
When did the smile turn fake?
When did holding hands become a duty?
When did sitting in the back of a car together become work?
When did talking become a part of the to-do list?
Do you stay?
Stay for what?
Leave for what?
There is no one here.
There is no one there.
A dream broken here

A mirage waiting there
Can soul mates be stolen? Do they leave?
"I like talking with her."
"I will never leave; I will do all my responsibilities."
Do you stick to a relationship that has turned mundane?
Why? And for whom?
Does it matter why, does it matter for whom?

by Baishakhi Mukherjee

68

Lovers In Black And White

Aru and I swept ourselves into
hidden closets,
marked by creaking floorboards
and pashmina shawls hung on old clotheslines.
We whispered secrets in there, Aru and I
and dreamt of lives where
we could whisper sweet nothings into
each other's ears all night~
but those things, as they say, were
just dreams, like dandelion seeds,
they fly far away too soon.
Aru and I, we hoped
oh - we dared to hope
that one day we might be able to carve poetry onto our skins
and maybe have children who spoke
in the languages of stars.
oh, we hoped. That maybe once, just once,
we could call each other as mine
Aru and I - we were born in a wrong time,
a time when girls cooked and cleaned
and didn't think of love
underneath kanjeevaram sarees.
A time when you whispered love
and mapped each other's backs
in darkness

Aru and I -
We were lovers in black and white times
rainbows weren't accepted back then.

by Asleena Argyris

69

I Killed My Love

What I did was what they told me, not my mind at work
Those procedures felt more robotic than conscious.
Do my choices define me? No, as I made none
It's a power possessed, by those hands not mine
It is either this or that, like nickel and dime.
They say its love, but I know not what's true
As I felt nothing of it, senselessly following rules.

I'm not happy how we met, unwilling to budge
You had lots to say unlike me, so I let you sway
Not my consort or counsel, yet so out of control
You bite the hand that fed you, a mad dog in ways
Forget the tragedy that followed, me trusting you
You defined love for me, to you I pinned my heart
They told me I'd be sorry, so I chose to break free
Regret flooding in now, karma has finally found me.

Their bonds to me shattered, I came home to you.
But in your arms stood instead, another distressed damsel,
Smothered by your affection, embracing the devil's kiss.
What was I to you then, for whom did I leave
The family that raised me, the master who fed
You put the blame on my change, and I beg to differ
You were my cup of hemlock, destruction bound to be.

Yet you are not my reason, but my beloved excuse
To find freedom from restraints, they never set for me.
How can I go back to them, how may I explain
The love that I had sought for was with them indeed.
Their love to me was their not-so-light commands,
Violently murdered by my ignorant acts
All that I can do now is to carry out its coffin,
To follow this lamented love, to my eternal bliss.

by Nirosha Tomy

70

My Window

I look out the bars of my window,
And see the green of the leaves,
With patches of blue sky-
Like random jigsaw pieces
In an unfinished puzzle
I can see the wind,
But not feel it.
I can sense the sound,
But not hear it.
I can touch the sunlight,
Almost
As I soar through the bars of my window-
In my mind,
Only in my mind
I sink back to reality.
I can smell defeat
And I reach out
And touch my truth-
Cold and brittle
Of bars and glass
And failure.

by Padma

71

Scared

by Prerna Agrawal

Hey! What happened? Are you scared? Scared of what? Scared of this darkness in this room or from someone? You can feel free to talk to me and share your fear. I am your dad, princess. Why are you getting scared of me" Said Mr. Allen to his daughter Sarah.

Mr. James Allen was one of the best writers in London. He has written many books and those books were famous all over the world. He was married to a beautiful girl named Clara. He had a daughter named Sarah. He loved his wife and daughter more than anyone in this world. Last year his wife died in a car accident. Sarah had been just eleven years old when her mother expired.

It was 9 pm when Mr. Allen came back home from one of his friend's party. He was about to ring the doorbell when he noticed that the door was open. He entered and called out for Sarah, but he didn't get any response. He went upstairs to look for her in her room, but she was not there. He was continuously calling out for her, but she didn't reply. Suddenly he heard a noise downstairs. He went there to look for her.

When he opened the door, he saw his daughter sitting in one of the corners of the room. It was a small storeroom with a few things about Sarah's mother. Sarah was sitting there all alone in that darkness. She was crying and shivering. Mr. Allen asked her, why she was sitting out there in that darkness, and he tried to enter that room, but she screamed and told him to stop. Mr. Allen got scared, he didn't understand what to do and what to say.

Ting-tong, the bell rang. Sarah jumped out in fear and tried to hide behind the boxes. "Shh! Shh! Don't get scared my child, it's just a doorbell" said Mr. Allen to Sarah. He went out to look who had come at this hour of the night. It was one of his friends. He had left his wallet in his friend's house when he went there to party. After taking his wallet from his friend, he shut the door and went back to his daughter, to where she was hiding.

"Hey! Are you scared? Scared of what? Scared of this darkness in this room or from someone? Tell me. You can feel free to talk to me and share your fear. I am your dad, princess. Why are you getting scared of me, but first come out of this room, from this darkness" said Mr. Allen and held out his hand for Sarah.

"No," Sarah screamed again. "All men are just the same. I am not coming out of here. Just go, leave me alone, I don't need anyone," said Sarah cryingly.

"What happened my child? Unless you tell me, how will I know what happened? How will I make things alright? All men are not the same, my princess. Now come on tell me what happened? I am here for you, your dad is here with you, princess" said Mr. Allen.

"Da-Da-Dad" Said Sarah more cryingly.

"Yes, my child," said Mr. Allen.

"How can this world be so cruel? Why did they do this to me? Why?" asked Sarah.

"What happened, my child? Who did what? Tell me, I am here with you, don't get scared. Come out of this darkness and tell me what happened that you're so scared" said Mr. Allen and held out his hand for Sarah. Finally, she caught his hand and came out of that room.

Mr. Allen was taken aback by looking at Sarah's condition. Her clothes were torn, her full body was covered with blood, she was crying and shivering. She could not even stand properly. She was not even in the condition to speak. Yes, you're correct, she was raped. The fifteen-year-old girl was raped by those monsters.

"How did all this happen, my child," asked Mr. Allen clearing his throat.

Sarah looked at her dad. Sobbing, she told him that when she was coming back from school, someone from the back pulled her and took her into a house. In that house, there was one more boy already waiting, and that boy was named Abraham, whom Sarah had slapped in front of the whole school for misbehaving with her, and now he was there to take revenge for that insult. How can a person be so cruel? She kept shouting and calling people for help, but no one came. She even begged them to leave her, but they didn't listen to her. They kept abusing her and she was continually raped by those monsters. She could not remember how many times or for how long. Finally, she made effort to run from that house and came to her home and hid in that room. Breathing loudly, Sarah fell on her knees.

Mr. Allen was in tears. With lots of courage, he came close to Sarah and hugged her. "Shh! Shh! Don't cry, my child. It's okay, everything will be fine, I am here with you" said Mr. Allen. After a few minutes "Come on, my child, get up. Be a brave girl and go freshen up. By then, I will prepare dinner for both of us" said Mr. Allen.

He took her to her room, and she went to freshen-up. Mr. Allen came down and started preparing dinner. When he placed all the dishes on the table Sarah came down. "Here is my brave girl, come, your favourite dinner is ready, let's eat," said Mr. Allen.

"Dad, I am not feeling hungry," said Sarah.

Mr. Allen made her sit on the chair and said "Listen, Sarah, there are many girls in this world, who have been raped and killed. So, do they stop living after being raped? Or do they stop eating and sit in their home thinking about what society will say? No, right? So, you're a brave girl, you're my girl, we will fight together for our rights and we will get justice. You're not alone, my child and it's not your fault, this experience is not what defines you as a human being. You're so much more than this my child. I don't care what people think about you or what they say. You're my child and I love you more than anything or anyone in this world, I don't care about people and even you should not care. Do whatever you feel like doing, don't think about others, ok? I am here with you, always"

It took her almost a year to get over this shock and start living her life again, but she did it. Those who raped Sarah were hanged as ordered by the judge. Now, Sarah is one of the best motivational speakers in London. Sarah was powerful not because she wasn't scared, but because she went on so strongly throughout all this despite the fear and even her father supported her a lot.

"Rape is one of the most terrible crimes on earth and it happens every few minutes. The problem with groups who deal with rape is that they try to educate women about how to defend themselves. What needs to be done is teaching men not to rape" said Kurt Cobain.

Seriously how can someone be so cruel as to rape a girl? Why do these monsters even exist in this world? Why can't all boys learn to respect girls and treat them properly? Rape isn't funny, so why is it that rape victims continue to be publicly mocked all over the country?

There are many girls like Sarah and Nirbhaya who are subject to such harrowing ordeals and it takes them years to get they justice they so rightly deserve. We are living in a society where politicians get away with murder, but such incidents often go unnoticed. When can we girls walk freely without the fear of being assaulted or worse?

72

Fat Nutmeg

by Divya Naveen

I remember my first day (of my life?) as the day on which I opened the car door to step into the hot sand on the beach. I was excited to remove my shoes and run towards the approaching waves. As my feet plunged into the golden yellow granulates, I felt like a princess, princess on a golden carpet.

I watched my Didi (elder sister) get into the water. I was hesitant. My father took me in his arms and stepped into the blizzards of the waves. The walk from the sand to the sea was dazzlingly beautiful and amazing... Or as a three-year-old remembers "Wanted to do it again and again". Another beautiful sunset unleashed.

My life was as normal as it could be for any other child, across the world, with the middle-class working parents trying to cope with the increasing demands of their children. I enjoyed it though, especially the time I spent with my father. My father being my role model, I looked up to him, a man of character, sensitive, helping anyone and everyone, with the best of personality and traits. My mother was just another working lady for me – managing between the household chores and her professional life as a banker. How strong a woman she was – unveils into another story.

Father took me wherever he went. I used to love being a pillion rider in his "Bajaj Chetak", which was later transformed into a red "Rajdoot" bike. It was like watching the world through Him. I always felt it as the world's best and everlasting moment, though I realized in the latter part of my life that nothing exists forever.

Summers and winters passed, I was no longer the three-year-old... I was growing up. I was hardly seven years old then. I had many friends in the neighbourhood - mostly boys. I loved playing cricket back then - with a paper ball, examination board, and the neighbouring grill gate as the wicket. 'Fours' were the next-door hits and 'Sixes' were the window cracks. And the team mostly scored 'Fours', which led furious owners to snatch the paper balls from us, being a nuisance. These were my so-called little "big achievements."

Closure: It was then that I learnt the first lesson of my life. The fat nutmeg has a crack – the most painful for her and her parents… the one that can never be fixed.

What went wrong? Did she not know about the good and the bad touches? Did she not know that not all friends and family are the same? Did she not know she had to tell her parents about it? Does being a 7-year-old give you enough maturity to find the answers for all of it, by yourself?

I am still wondering.

Meet The Co-Authors

Sushree Diya Om

Sushree Diya Om is a monk and a disciple of Om Swami. A former model, actress, and LLB Law graduate from London. After overcoming many of life's hurdles, in 2015, at the height of her success, she moved to the Himalayas to answer her spiritual calling. She now dedicates her life to serving others.

Samyuktha Ramachandran

As an individual that flourishes within the world of creativity, poetry to Samyuktha is a way to express her thoughts and emotions. Through her work, she communicates words of empowerment, strength, and courage that can resonate in the hearts of others. Her voice can be heard through her poetry.

Baishakhi Mukherjee

A happy person in love with life, who loves books, dark chocolates, and coffee. Baishakhi is a single parent of an active happy 3-year-old. Her mantra: If life doesn't give you reasons to smile... laugh instead. All her writings have one thing in common: life is not about existing but living.

Sarvesh Shyam

Sarvesh Shyam is a marketing maverick who started his career in the finance industry with Goldman Sachs. Writing has been his passion and he dreams of capturing people's imagination with his words, making a positive difference to the community, and inducing social change through empathy & creativity.

Arthi P

Arthi is an IT professional and has travelled to many places outside India in her career of 20 years. She is an avid reader and has a keen interest in creating poetry with specific themes. She believes in women's empowerment but with the right intent.

Suhas Ramegowda

A typical corporate droid chasing materialistic dreams turned mountain dweller. For over a decade, Suhas Ramegowda lived a mechanical life until he realised there's a way to be simply alive. What started as an exploration of this path led to a more meaningful existence among the mountains.

Chantal Espitalier – Noel

Mauritian born Chantal is artistic, unconventional, and passionate about self-transformational work, tarot, and meditation. She is currently writing her debut novel and enjoys spending time in the Himalayas in spiritual practices.

Deepa Ragunathan

A software developer by day, Deepa spends her free time with food and books, either voraciously reading every book she can find, or writing short stories and long poems onto the empty pages of the notebooks she collects.

Sitara Kumbale

Sitara graduated from college recently and currently works as an Analyst. She tries to capture the nuances of everyday life and the heartstring-tugging range of human emotion through poetry and prose. Apart from writing, Sitara also enjoys baking, volunteering, and travelling.

Sumati Mohan

Sumati is a fun-loving and light-hearted person. She loves to travel with her family and friends during her free time. Sumati also enjoys gardening and loves to binge on spicy Indian street food. She has 20+ years of experience in global Sales & Marketing with leading IT Services firms.

Nirosha Tomy

As a political science graduate, living amidst the cultural diversity of the national capital Nirosha Tomy uses her personal experiences and that of the people around her to create a perfect blend of fact and fiction to produce an authentic literary work. She hopes to inspire and influence others to think, through her carefully curated writings.

Dr. R. Uma Sharma

She is a Hindi professor who has more than 18 years of experience teaching students of different age groups. She has her motivational YouTube channel with weekly content to motivate students. She is a very energetic person and is always willing to learn new skills.

Lakshmi Priyanga M

Lakshmi Priyanga is a law student. She expresses her feelings through music and art. She's a fun person and her dogs and her family mean the world to her. She believes that everything has a purpose for its existence. Her motto in life is simple, "HAKUNA MATATA".

Rakshita Nagaraj

Rakshita Nagaraj is a second year Masters's student. She is a pharmacologist in the making. A huge science fanatic, intersectional feminist, and an animal lover. She is a fun person to grab a coffee or book or wine with.

Amala L

Amala loves to be a feminist! Being an introvert, she befriended her pen to create heart-warming random snippets. Her ambitions of becoming an economist never let her settle. Surrounded by good souls, she aspires to create an impact on this world!

Maria Mappilassery

Maria is a poetess and artist. The structure of her poems favours emotions and an empathetic sense among the readers. She is an alumna of Loyola College Chennai, a post-graduate in English Literature, and holds a Diploma in Multimedia. Born in Kerala, she currently lives in Adelaide with her family.

Neha Prashar Verma

Neha is a market researcher, a traveller, a military wife, and a mother. In her journey of writing stories, blogs, and poems, she has created various pearls with her literary skills. She loves to read in solace with her thoughts. Her works are inspired by daily life, emotions, fiction, and travels.

Padma

Padma is a mother of two, who is currently rediscovering her passion for poems and writing. She believes in the power of words and finds writing cathartic.

Aryaman Chakraborty

Young, passionate, easy-going, friendly are some of the adjectives which describe our new budding teenage author "Aryaman." When he is taking a break, he is most happy reading Action/Fiction books. This story was inspired by his love for fiction and took momentum. Our young author is here to stay!

Minnu Ranjith

She is a homemaker, mother of two, YouTuber and likes to go with the flow of life. She possesses a credible simplicity that attracts enthusiastic admirers. Good food, romantic movies, and songs always pep up her mood. She is graceful, sensitive, impulsive, independent, sympathetic, and sees her life as an expression of her deep inner creativity.

Namrada Varshini

Exploring the world within her mind, while capturing life into focus where it is beautiful through the minuscule lens and the tip of her pen! She dives into a plethora of creations and yes, she is Namrada Varshini, pulsing through the penned down words.

Nalini Vipin

Born in Kerala and brought up in Bangalore, Nalini has lived most of her life in the romantic deserts of the Gulf. A teacher by profession, she was an active member of the NGO Indian Ladies Association of Bahrain, also its President in the Sneha Silver Jubilee year 2012. She takes pride in being a member of Bahrain Poetry Club and WMC Toastmasters Club, which helped her to reinvent herself as a budding poet and orator. Travelling, interior designing, painting, and dance occupy her free hours, but Poetry is her passion. Writing poetry is her way of billing her unadulterated thoughts. "My poems usually revolve around love, life, relationships, and societal issues," says Nalini. Her poems can be read on the Instagram handle @Scintillabynalini

Christina Triplett-Wagenknecht

Christina Triplett-Wagenknecht is a published poet originally from Florida. Since 2008, she has been writing from Germany, where she lives with her husband. She has co-authored many poetry anthologies and has invented the poetry form called, "The Triptych Triplett", which is found on her Instagram profile, @ladyleighpoetry.

Divya Om Manoharan

Divya Om Manoharan lives in the Himalayan foothills at an ashram. After falling into the spiritual path, she now lives each day in service of her God and Truth. She believes that compassion and laughter are the hallmarks of a peaceful, content life. Her motto is, "Love, love. And love some more."

Riya Om

Riya is from Ludhiana, Punjab. She is the author of two poetry books "Shayarana si hai yeh Zindagi" and "Mere Ehsas". She is currently pursuing her MBA in finance.

Sujitha Ryali

Sujitha is an Indian, living in Sweden. "Never give up even when there is no hope" is what defines her in short, A phenomenal person. While doing an incredible job as an Automotive engineer, she built her passion for writing to do more in life along with her regular job. She started as a content writer & working to be an International Author & film writer. You can Reach her at: https://instagram.com/sujiryali.

Nitya Bhatia

Nitya started writing poems from the age of 16 and since then with her poetry touched upon several socially relevant issues like bullying, body positivity, women empowerment with the intent of spreading awareness. She is pursuing a diploma in Spanish and dreams of publishing her book someday.

Ambika Rao

She's a first-time poet and a published children's writer.

Maria Wynnyckyj

Maria Wynnyckyj currently works at a state college and is a writer /poet. She is a proud mother of three grown children and 2 grandchildren. Maria currently resides in the United States of America. Maria is inspired by art in all its forms because of what it reveals to her.

Christine J

Christine wishes to remain anonymous!

Renee Mary Jetto

Renee is a retired teacher who loves poetry, plays and movies.

Soham Maliye

Soham is a bibliophile and an omnivert. She is a hobbyist writer and a blogger who finds solace in books.

Maxine Mathew

Maxine Mathew is an ardent bibliophile. When not swamped with her work as a content manager in a market research firm, she loves to cozy up on her sofa with a book and a strong cup of tea. Her other interests include reading Shakespearean tragedies, painting, and binging on sitcoms and Jane Austen-esque period dramas.

Komal R D

By profession, Komal R D is a Computer Science graduate and by passion, she is an ardent reader and a writer in making. She believes hobby defines a person and hence channelizes them in her Instagram blog @pickupbooks, where she helps people find 'their right book match' through her book reviews.

Munmun Aidasani

Munmun Aidasani, Chartered Financial Analyst by profession, hails from the city of lakes, Bhopal (India) currently residing in Dubai (U. A. E). She loves wearing many hats. She is an avid and a versatile writer, an author, and a blogger. A dreamer with a passion to establish her own benchmark in writing. When she is not writing, she indulges her children, husband and loved ones with sumptuous food, with a curious mind trying to witness art in everything possible. Her inner wisdom of being empathic and caring towards her loved ones makes her a wonderful human being to be around. She loves writing fiction as well as non-fiction articles, inspired by real events. She wants to branch out into different genres of writing as she believes in versatility. She can be reached on Instagram @munmunaidasani, on Facebook @Rising-Mom and via Email @aidasanimunmun@gmail.com

Divya Naveen

Divya — an adventure freak, who is passionate about anything and everything she does. She loves travelling and dreams to fly a fighter plane. She believes that there is something good in everyone and considers herself to be a gullible person. She is someone who radiates happiness and positivity around her and believes in the fact that "Whatever happens it is for one's good."

Joshuanna Woods

Joshuanna Woods is the youngest of four siblings born into a loving home. She lived her life sheltered and it seemed to be engaged in thoughts of unworthiness. At 13 her mother passed and sparked rebellion as she felt God betrayed her by taking her protector and guidance. This sent her spiralling on a beautiful journey of self-worth.

Soumya Gudiyella

Soumya Gudiyella has a doctorate in Chemical Engineering. Soumya has two passions, chemistry, and stories. She is contributing to her 'chemistry' side by working for an automobile company. She is exploring her 'stories' side by reading a ton of books and writing stories and novels. Read more about her interests at www.soumsgudiyella.com

Tejasvi Rajesh

Tejasvi is in the final year of law school. She loves dogs, photography, and travelling. You'll often find her talking to and petting her dog. Cosy corners, a mug of coffee, and her favourite playlist are all she needs to wind down and relax!

Vidya Shivaram

Vidya Shivaram is an Educator with a passion for Kannada literature and farming. She grew up in a small village of Udupi Dist., in Karnataka. Much of her experiences and inspiration for the work she does comes from her time spent in her hometown. She has been a Kannada educator for 10 years.

Sabhyata Bhandari

She is just an ordinary girl with big dreams.

Asleena Argyris

A starry-eyed girl obsessively in love with books, nature, and art. Yearns to live in a place with rolling hills and enough trees. Usually found in leafy balconies and among bookshelves smelling of nostalgia and memories. Hopes to talk to trees and practice magic, one day.

Anju Anil

Born and brought up in Kerala and settled in the IT hub of India, Anju is a true Keralite who always longs for the greenery of Kerala. She is a software professional who likes to travel around the world to learn from different cultural perspectives. She likes to write stories that depict the tenacity of human life to thrive and to move on.

Prerna Agrawal

She is a girl for whom simplicity is the key to happiness. She likes coffee the way she likes herself: Sweet and strong. She believes God has given us one life and we should not waste that on worrying and that we must live our life to the fullest and inspire others.

INKFEATHERS PUBLISHING

India's Most Author Friendly Publishing House

Stay updated about latest books, anthologies, events, exclusive offers, contests, product giveaways and other things that we do to support authors.

 Inkfeathers Publishing

 @InkfeathersPublishing

 @_Inkfeathers

 @Inkfeathers

 Inkfeathers.com

We'd love to connect with you!